Construction Companion to Briefing

David Hyams

RIBA Publications

© David Hyams 2001

Published by RIBA Companies Ltd, which trades under the name of
'RIBA Publications', Construction House, 56–64 Leonard Street, London EC2A 4JX

ISBN 1 85946 088 7

Product Code: 21661

Publisher: Mark Lane
Editor: Lionel Browne
Series Editor: David Chappell
Commissioning Editor: Matthew Thompson
Design and typesetting: Bettina Hovgaard-Petersen

Printed and bound by Hobbs the Printers, Hampshire

Contents

Foreword

This is the first of a series of guides being produced by RIBA Publications under the general heading of *Construction Companion*. They are intended to be compact and accessible guides written in plain English, but each one authoritative in its own right.

The *RIBA Plan of Work* now lists 'Strategic Briefing' as stage B. This includes more than just briefing, but no amount of title changing will alter the fact that the briefing exercise is the single most important function in the construction process. The process may be quite short and finite, or it may continue during the whole of the development of the design. The brief is the problem to which the building is the answer. No amount of effort expended on the design will matter if the problem is inadequately formulated and understood. An elementary instruction to examination candidates is to read the question carefully before attempting an answer. An architect with an incomplete brief is like a candidate who only half reads the question. Time spent on the briefing process saves abortive work at the design stages.

Yet there appears to be very little order in the way in which architects approach the task of securing the brief. Many architects treat it as a casual endeavour, an almost unnecessary precursor to the design stage. At its most basic, architects who produce building designs that do not satisfy their clients' requirements, because they have not bothered to get an accurate brief, have not earned their fees. Worse, they delay the whole process.

It is essential to take a systematic approach to briefing, although the character of the system will vary with the size and complexity of the project. There are only two ways to handle briefing: the right and the wrong way. Techniques may differ, and it is appropriate that they do differ to suit the project, the temperament of the client and of the architect. But it is important not to stray from basic principles. For this purpose, checklists are invaluable.

David Hyams has specialised in briefing. He has produced what is likely to become a little classic of its kind. The book sets out the basic principles and explains the process of briefing before dealing with the characters involved and their respective roles. Techniques are explored, and the reader is shown how to adapt the techniques to suit different projects. Detailed checklists are supplied and, to show how the whole thing comes to together, the book ends with case studies of three very different projects. Adopting these procedures should ensure that briefing becomes an absorbing as well as an essential part of the design process.

David Chappell BA(Hons Arch) MA(Arch) MA(Law) PhD RIBA
Series Editor

Introduction

Building in Britain costs up to a third more than in America or the rest of Europe. Not only does this place a heavy burden on the economy and hinder adaptability and change, but also the resulting buildings are often inappropriate and inconvenient for their users. Sir Michael Latham, in his report on improving the efficiency of the building industry, identified various factors that contribute to the high cost and poor user satisfaction of new buildings in this country.1 Poor briefing came high on his list.

Time spent deciding what is required before designing is infinitely less expensive and more effective than changes made during design, let alone during or after construction. The closer a project comes to construction the higher will be the cost of change, and the smaller the opportunity to revise decisions.

Architects in Britain have always taken instruction from their clients, but rarely systematically. This book is a short practical guide to systematic briefing: how to do consciously what has until now been done intuitively.

The following scenario may well be familiar. The clients arrive with a new project and a one-page brief consisting of a list of the main spaces, a target cost, a possible site, and some more or less random objectives for the building. The design architect evaluates the site, discusses a budget, perhaps consults a book or journal articles on new buildings of the same type, and starts to design. After some soft pencil work, usually related to fitting the building to the site, a design emerges. The client likes it, but requests some changes. These changes, and the many that follow, are made (sometimes grudgingly), and the drawings slowly evolve through trial and error into a design. During this process, the architect sees his or her role as defending the integrity of the original design concept against all comers – clients, planners, quantity surveyor and engineers. When a more or less satisfactory compromise has been reached, the final design is presented to the clients. The question implicitly put to the clients at this point is, 'Do you like it?' This places the clients in a difficult position. They can say 'Yes', 'No', or 'Yes but...' The decision is far from clear without the benefit of a structured definition of what was to be achieved.

How much simpler it would be if the building were evaluated against such a definition. Then the decision would be a matter of which objectives had not been met, which had, with what success and at what cost. The question 'Do you like it?' is a good one and valid, but 'liking' is about the quality of delight, *after* the essential requirements have been met.

But, the architect may argue, what happens to creativity and the creative process if the architect's imagination is hemmed in by constraints? All that happens is that design is now viewed as the answer to defined needs. It is still also about response to the site, and about individual creativity, but the priority is now to provide space that meets defined needs. The architect could see the brief as a spur to creativity rather than a limitation.

Without that mysterious creative spark architecture is not architecture, but unless needs are defined and buildings are designed that meet them, architects fail not only their clients but also building users.

Briefing is about that definition; it is about defining the problem to which the design will be a solution. A well-written brief simplifies much of the early sorting out of design objectives. Suppose that, instead of leaping to one concept, the architect first develops a number of concepts, tests and refines them against a sytematic brief, and perhaps works up three ideas in parallel. They are then evaluated, and a preferred option is selected. This book describes briefing as a process that is distinct and yet integral to the design process, avoiding wilfulness and giving clients what they have decided, after proper consideration, they need and want.

The construction industry in Britain delivers projects of a vast range of sizes, from kitchen extensions to buildings that accommodate thousands of people, and architects are involved at every level. This book attempts to cover briefing for the whole range; the basic principles are the same. Using this book, architects working on smaller projects will be able to simplify and create a briefing process suitable for each project. At the same time, the coverage aims to be sufficiently comprehensive to support work on the largest projects.

The first three chapters set out the principles and process of briefing. Chapters 4 and 5 discuss the roles of participants and introduce the place of sustainability in briefing. Chapters 6, 7 and 8 describe a 'tool-box' of techniques to use during briefing. Chapters 9 to 12 consist of annotated checklists for various stages of the process. Finally, to demonstrate how all that has gone before can be applied, Chapter 13 describes case histories of three small and medium-sized projects.

A word about use of language: 'briefing consultant' is used throughout to refer to the distinct role that an architect adopts when writing a brief, in order to distinguish that from the role of designer. 'Clients' are usually referred to in the plural to include the various roles and people included in the client team in all but the smallest project. Most clients represent an 'organisation', and this word is used to include family, government, and voluntary organisations, services, and of course companies – the organisational model of the era.

I want to thank Matthew Thompson, commissioning editor, for his endless patience and positive encouragement. I am also extremely grateful for the help I have received from many in the writing of this book, and particularly from Judy Kearns and Professor Susan Roaf for their time and care in commenting on the manuscript, the latter providing essential input on sustainability.

1 Sir Michael Latham, Constructing the Team: joint review of procurement and contractual arrangements, HMSO, London, 1994.

1 A problem-solving approach

This chapter describes the central logic of the briefing process. It applies to any size of project and at each stage in the project. The chapters that follow describe technique in greater detail, but this chapter introduces the principles underlying the process as a whole. The chapter discusses three basic ideas in briefing:

- a problem-solving process
- a six-step briefing process
- an adaptable process

1.1 A problem-solving process

Design is, among other things, a problem-solving process. The idea of problem solving is particularly useful when the architect is faced with a complex problem to which there is no immediately obvious solution. It involves pausing to organise and plan before rushing to a solution. The first step is to define the problem itself very clearly. A problem defined is amenable to solution, whereas an undefined problem is just a mess.

A building may mean many things to different people – a design that lifts the spirit, a landmark in the city, a successful capital investment, a convenient space to work – but in its original conception it was an answer to a complex set of problems. No one goes to the immense cost and effort of building without there being a very clear argument in favour of it. Briefing is the process of exposing this argument, probing its integrity and laying it out clearly for examination. It is the justification for building something specific that meets defined needs. It is doing consciously and explicitly what architects have always done, but often unconsciously.

Briefing is defining the question to which the design is an answer, the one answer chosen from among the many possible. Like the fit of a glove on the hand, the more clearly the problem is defined, the more closely a design can satisfy the requirements.

A clear distinction is necessary between defining the problem and finding solutions to it: that is, between *briefing* and *design*. The brief need not be complete in every detail before any design work starts, but each phase of design (whether of a whole building or just an element of it) needs to be preceded by a process of problem definition. This is clearly a move away from the all-too-common approach of jumping to a design solution early in the process and then putting the design through a number of modifications until everyone is satisfied that the best compromise between various conflicting objectives has been achieved. In this sense it demands of designers a small shift in attitude. The problem-solving approach alternates continually between problem definition and solution as each aspect of design is tackled. In this way, problem definition becomes an integral though distinct part of the design process: definition–solution, definition–solution.

Problem-solving methodology derives from systems analysis, and is closely allied to the logic found in computer software design. It consists typically of:

- defining a goal – the overall aim of the project
- defining objectives – detailed, measurable milestones towards attaining the goal
- identifying options – possible approaches that fulfil the objectives
- evaluating options – assessing the costs and benefits of each option
- selecting a preferred option

The selected option is not yet a design solution; it is an agreed problem definition.

Put another way, the briefing consultant transforms intractable problems into tractable ones by finding conceptual solutions that are problem redefinitions, and certainly not physical design solutions. Reframing the question, or uncovering the real questions beneath the apparent confusion, is a sort of conceptual solution but not a physical design solution.

1.2 A six-step process

Translated into practical briefing method, the problem-solving approach described above is expanded into a six-step process:

1 scope
2 role
3 activities
4 draft requirements
5 testing
6 approval

The principles of these six steps are set out below, and described in more detail in Chapters 2 and 3. Detailed checklists of questions to be asked at each stage are in Chapters 9 to 12.

1.2.1 Defining the scope

Briefing starts with a definition of the breadth, focus, scope, parameters or borders of the briefing exercise. In all but the smallest project this will probably require several discussions with the client group: clients and brief writer will agree what work is to be done and what areas are to be left untouched.

1.2.2 Role

The role statement describes *what the user organisation is for*: its purpose, aim, goal, remit or mission. It can be quite short – a couple of lines – even if the building will be large and complex. In the early stages a role statement may appear pointlessly obvious, but it is the key to the logic of everything that follows. It is a statement of the role of the occupying organisation, department or workgroup, not a statement of the role of the building. Space has no function other than to support the aims of the organisation it accommodates, whether that organisation is a two-person family or a multinational company. Guidelines and standards will be set for the way in which this is to be done in the requirements section.

For a complex organisation the role statement may take the form of a primary goal and a number of objectives that detail its key aspects.

Example
A hospital may have the overall aim of providing tertiary health care services to a specific geographic region, and objectives covering the various surgical, medical and support departments, education and research.

The role statement is the touchstone for evaluating the brief and the design that flows from it.

Example
A business looking for an office building in a city centre location includes a cafeteria in its list of requirements despite the numerous cafés and sandwich bars nearby. The question is not how strongly this group of managers want a cafeteria but whether the cafeteria is consistent with the company's role statement, which may contain staff welfare policy objectives for staff amenities.

1.2.3 Activities

In order to fulfil the building's stated role, its users undertake activities, operations, work, or tasks. The activity statement is a description of what will go on in the building – the operations that the building will be designed to support. Activities include a schedule of staff numbers and categories, a chart of the management structure, the characteristics of people visiting the building to receive services, descriptions of the key processes and materials involved, and other explanations useful to the designer.

1.2.4 Draft requirements

Up to this point, information has been taken from the clients, analysed, interpreted and represented. In this step, the characteristics of the space necessary to support the activities are formulated. This is the information that the design team are most interested in. It includes a space budget listing functional spaces, quantities of repeated spaces and their areas. It also details the required relationships between spaces, and defines the characteristics of spaces, benchmark standards for services and environmental comfort, and any other specific design guidelines.

1.2.5 Testing

So far the brief has been generated from the intrinsic needs of the activities and operations of the building users in fulfilment of the organisational goal and objectives. It is now at the stage where what have been perhaps ideal requirements are tested against real-world constraints. This is not to say that the process has been out of touch with reality up to this point, but the focus has not been primarily on constraints.

The criteria for testing are, briefly, as follows:

- Will it fit? Is there space available to accommodate the defined requirements?
- How much will it cost? Does this cost represent good value for the organisation?
- Is it affordable and financially feasible? Is there a business case?
- Are real needs clearly distinguished from mere desires?
- Is the argument given in the brief internally consistent?

These and other similar issues will vary in detail with the unique features of each project and with stages in project development, but the principles remain fairly constant for all projects.

One could ask why testing is introduced only at this relatively late stage in the briefing process. Is there not a danger that the client group will be led so far away from reality by discussing their needs in an abstract, ideal sense that the testing stage brings them back to earth with a hard bump, and they become disillusioned with a process that allowed them to hope for the unachievable? Is it not better to begin right from the start with what is sensible and feasible, and base a brief on that? This concern is valid, but there are answers to it.

First, the process is designed in this way in order to get at what is really *needed*. If needs are defined in terms of constraints, there is a greater danger that the real needs will never be articulated. It is better to start by defining what is really needed, before testing its feasibility, than to limit consideration to what at first sight appears possible according to conventional thinking. Fresh solutions come about only when conventional thinking is challenged. Feasibility is partly a subjective judgement, which can change when real needs are clarified in the light of their measurable value. The site and the eventual building will support the activities and role, not the other way round. It is quite possible that one of the results of the testing stage will be that previous ideas about the site or existing building are drastically revised.

Second, it is good practice to avoid developing unrealistic expectations by warning users that they will not necessarily achieve everything they ask for. Clients and users are quite prepared to discuss possibilities on this understanding. They recognise that their ideal may be limited by cost and other constraints. If questions are not asked, the real needs will never be discovered, and creative design solutions, which spring from a deep understanding of the problem, will be lost. Testing is never too far from the briefing process, tempering rather than restricting discussion and providing an anchor to reality. It is a question of balance, tact and some delicacy in leading the discussion to a conclusion.

The outcome of testing is a series of amendments and revisions to the original draft requirements and the draft brief document as a whole. If the brief has been well constructed these amendments will be few, but there are always some. The consultant has to be suspicious if there are none, as this indicates a lack of attention and commitment on the part of the clients. By this stage, the clients should be committed to the brief and to the project. If they are not, the project will surely unravel before long.

1.2.6 Approval

Without client approval, the project goes no further. Approval authorises the revised final brief document to go forward as the basis for design. If the clients' top decision-makers have been involved in the process of developing the brief, they will understand the difficulties that have been resolved, and will be committed to the result. Then approval should present no problem. Without approval, the brief is one more consultancy report gathering dust on the shelf. With approval signed off, preferably formally in writing on a prepared form, the project moves forward to the design phase, backed by commitment to allocate funds.

Figure 1.1 summarises the six-step process.

1. SCOPE What is the problem?

    2. ROLE What is the client organisation for?

        3. ACTIVITIES What do they do to fulfil their role?

            4. REQUIREMENTS What do they need to support what they do?

                5. TESTING Is the draft brief feasible?

                    6. APPROVAL Does the brief go forward?

Figure 1 1 The six-step process

1.3 An adaptable process

Briefs can be written at various levels of detail. The problem can be summarised lightly, worked through in moderate depth, or spelled out in great detail. The choice depends on a number of factors:

- the size and complexity of the project
- whether the building type is well known and documented
- the wishes of the clients and their advisors
- the capacity of the clients to participate in a detailed briefing process
- the time and budget available for the briefing exercise

The brief focuses on unusual issues, those that a design architect might not expect – the new, the exceptional, the particular requirement. Issues that are clearly understood by all concerned can be summarised or omitted altogether. It is still advisable to look through a comprehensive checklist to ensure that nothing has been missed. Even in cases where in-depth briefing seems inappropriate, it is worthwhile looking through the checklists in Chapters 9 to 12 for the relevant issues to develop a customised project checklist.

1.3.1 Commercial developments

Where the ultimate user organisation is not known, because the project is a commercial speculative development, briefing takes the form of market research. The most successful commercial developments are those that have tested the market to assess demand and have analysed the specific needs of known tenant types. For instance, there may be a demand in a certain location for offices for legal firms, for media production companies, or for back office functions of large companies, each of which has very different space requirements. Having assessed demand, the consultant defines a generic brief for tenants of the selected target group. The brief is developed from interviews with typical companies in that category. An interview questionnaire is used, following a modified version of the six-step process described above.

1.3.2 Understanding existing operations

Where the building type is well known and documented, and where, for instance, additional space is to be provided for an existing operation, it makes sense to analyse the existing use of space. This is done by survey and by interview. Survey data is essential in broadening an understanding of the organisation and its way of using space. If it is used as the primary basis for defining the requirements for new space, it is possible to lose sight of space as a service supporting operations that in turn support organisational objectives. There is a danger in assuming that an organisation will continue to operate in the way it does at present, and that new space should replicate present arrangements. The six-step briefing process avoids that danger. If existing space is found by survey, interview and subsequent discussion to work well, its strong features will be incorporated into the brief and its weaker features will be strengthened.

1.3.3 Simplified briefing

Small, uncomplicated buildings need short simple briefs, and the reverse is equally true. A brief for a confectionery kiosk may be a mere half page and mention everything necessary.

Some building types have been extensively studied and documented, and, provided one allows for changes in technology, markets and working practices, information from the literature can be used to supplement a simplified briefing process.

Where building types have become standardised in layout and design, and accepted throughout an industry, a full briefing exercise is not necessary; a cursory check on requirements will suffice before continuing with minor amendments to the design. Examples of standardised building types are petrol service stations, fast food outlets, speculative housing and some low-cost chain hotels. Continuous development and refinement of design have occurred through many projects over a number of years. In these cases there will be a standardised brief document that specifies spaces very precisely and defines the common brand image. Project briefing will focus on the size of the functional components and any unique features that distinguish the particular project or reflect changing operational practice and technology.

In some cases the building itself is more important than the functions within it. Historic buildings, churches and architectural masterpieces fall within this group. Usually, the integrity of the existing building can be taken as a fixed constraint in a brief for detailed refitting.

In cases such as processing plants, industrial warehouses, manufacturing operations, farm and horticultural buildings the brief may be written in terms of process analysis and engineering performance specification, with minimal focus on the needs of the few people required to tend the operation. It might be appropriate for an architect, as opposed to an engineer, to carry out a very light briefing exercise for populated areas of such buildings, where people do not have the major role in operations.

The nature of the clients also influences the depth of briefing. If the clients are unwilling to commission a briefing exercise, or to make time available to participate in it, then briefing can't be done with any degree of thoroughness. On some projects the clients are committed to commissioning new space but are not prepared to participate in detailed decision-making. In these cases it is reasonable for the consultant to make assumptions as to what is required, based on the best available information and on best practice in comparable buildings.

1.3.4 In-depth briefing

A thorough and extensive briefing exercise is particularly important for projects where environmental and planning criteria are critical to support the operations of building users. These are buildings where accurate space standards will make a big difference to costs, where temperature and humidity controls vary from room to room, where circulation of various categories of user and materials around the building is crucial, where a particular environmental quality is specified for individual spaces, or where many types of equipment require special mechanical services. Hospitals are perhaps the most extreme case of a demanding environment, but research laboratories and some forms of high-tech manufacturing are equally demanding. Museums, art galleries, law courts and performance spaces are each demanding in other ways. Such buildings particularly benefit from this briefing approach because of the mix of building user issues and servicing requirements, and the importance of circulation routes and relationships between spaces. They are usually large and complex, and often subject to frequent growth and internal change. Offices also demand a specific form of briefing, not because they are particularly technically sophisticated, but because of the substantial gains to be made through productivity improvements and reduced building operating costs.

Large organisations with substantial building programmes will often have standard in-house briefing documents. These need to be checked for completeness and for changes in circumstances. Where one-off building types arise, the clients' own professional project managers will expect a rigorous briefing analysis.

From time to time new building types emerge for which there is little or no precedent, and where a thorough briefing study is indicated. In the last few years, for instance, learning resource centres and call centres have come into this category.

1.3.5 Adaptability and loose fit

Not every space needs to be as tailored to its use as the proverbial aircraft cockpit. A degree of looseness and lower density will allow for both day-to-day adaptability and longer-term change and growth. It is possible to so pack the building envelope with functions that there is no opportunity for growth and change. This is a question not so much of writing a brief that is too detailed, as of underestimating the need for a small amount of unassigned floor area in the building to accommodate inevitable change.

Adaptability of structure and fabric is a similar but separate issue. There is a wisdom in writing into briefs a requirement for structures that accommodate unforeseen change. There are gains both for long-term construction costs and for sustainability in robust, loose-fit, adaptable buildings. For example, Georgian town-houses are famously adaptable, and have been recycled through numerous uses. There are limits to adaptability, though, and they must be clearly stated in the brief. There used to be a vogue for multifunction spaces in buildings for education, community and performance, which were designed to support so many varied activities that they didn't support any of them adequately. Be wary of situations where clients ask for quantities of movable partitioning. The ability to extend a building in the future, whether vertically or horizontally, provides a further degree of adaptability that, if required, needs to be identified in the brief.

1.3.6 Adaptability, choice and the future

There is no single right brief for a particular building. There is nothing absolute about the requirements that finally end up in a brief. The brief is a considered assessment of what will best suit clients and building users, given the many constraints of the situation. It is the result of studies, surveys, discussions, assumptions, projections, and many judgements. The danger is that the rationality of briefing is a linear one, with cause and effect seen in a simplistic way that never works out in real life. The future is of course unknowable; it is clear that it will not unfold precisely as projected and very likely will diverge significantly. All the brief can do is reduce risk by reducing uncertainty, and this is done by exercising choice in a way that leaves options open rather than restricting future possibilities. That is looking at the problem from a proper, defensive, risk-management point of view. At the same time it can be viewed from a more positive and creative point of view, in which the consultant asks him or herself: following the trends, energies and possibilities latent within this client organisation, what is the best way in which it could develop, and what serviced space would best facilitate that development?

Risk and possibility are complementary viewpoints, which require judgement. Taken together they provide a powerful framework for briefing.

2 Sequences

Except on the smallest of projects, briefing is a repetitive activity. It is not done once only at the start of the project. People take decisions best when the issues are crucial and timely for them. Decisions taken too far ahead lack a realistic context, and are unresponsive to actual events as they unfold. So briefing is usually sequenced to provide packages of relevant information as the project progresses. It is better to plan the sequence consciously from the start than to go ahead with whatever information happens to be available. As a project develops, decisions made early on set the context for decision-making on more detailed issues; it is a process that requires an ordered approach. The sequences of briefing respond to two distinct areas of decision-making: the *procurement* process and the *design* process. In addition, decisions in each of these two areas affect the other, and the sequence has been arranged to provide the necessary coordination.

2.1 Briefing and procurement

Table 2.1 Briefing within the procurement process [1]

Procurement stage	Briefing documents prepared	Purpose of briefing	Other non-briefing tasks
1. Getting started	• Statement of need	• The clients' own initial identification of need	• Nominate client project sponsor and client project coordinator
	• Option appraisal	• Consultants define and evaluate options for meeting the need	• Seek professional advice
		• Clients develop the business case	• Confirm the business case
2. Defining the project	• Strategic brief	• Clients' internal project justification	• Clients develop their internal plan for procuring and managing the project – the project execution plan • Decide contracts
3. Assembling the team			• Select project team
4. Designing and constructing	• Project brief	• Briefing instructions to the design and construction team, usually in at least two parts	• Develop and complete concept design, detailed design and production information • Start construction • Review progress and quality • Manage and resolve any problems
5. Completion and evaluation	• Post-project evaluation	• Assess the process, measuring building performance against the brief and user satisfaction	• Complete construction and commissioning • Complete the project

Table 2.1 describes the sequencing of briefing tasks in relation to the management of the procurement process as a whole. It applies to projects of all sizes. The arrangement is sufficiently robust to support projects of thousands of square metres, in which case each briefing document produced will consist of a substantial formal report. At the other end of the scale, a couple of sentences or paragraphs might suffice to record the briefing process in a project of tens of square metres. What is important is consideration and some documentation at each stage. The briefing documents are each described below. They are:

- statement of need
- option appraisal
- strategic brief
- project brief
- post-project evaluation

2.1.1 Statement of need

The statement of need is the clients' own first effort to define what is required of the proposed new space. On a small project it will be very informal; on a larger one, and especially on a public sector project, it will take the shape of a formal report. It will usually be prepared by the clients themselves. It is essential background for the consultant's briefing process and, if it does not exist, probably the first thing the consultant needs to do is to piece one together. This can be done by having the clients answer the questions given in the checklist in Chapter 9, during interviews or in meetings with the client group. The checklist is generic, and contains questions that may not be relevant to every project. If it is written by and for the clients, some of the issues may be generally understood and will not need restating except to explain how the project fits within organisational objectives and the business plan. The consultant reviews any written information, and makes a preliminary walk-around survey of any existing facilities to understand the context of the study, the quality of existing building stock, and the clients' habits of building use. In some situations more detailed, specialised surveys will be required.

2.1.2 Option appraisal

The aim of an option appraisal is to identify ways of meeting the requirements defined in the statement of need, as well as possible sites, and to test them. This process, part financial feasibility and part design feasibility, is carried out by the clients' business case team with or without the assistance of an external consultant. In the terminology of Chapter 1, it constitutes the 'testing' step for the statement of need. The options to be investigated may include reusing existing space in new ways or extending it, leasing additional space, and partial or total relocation. They may also include redesigning or contracting out operations so as to avoid the need for additional space. One option should always be to do nothing. The costs and benefits of each option are assessed and compared.

2.1.3 Strategic brief

If briefing in general informs design, the strategic brief is an exception in that it is not concerned with design in the sense that an architect would recognise it. The strategic brief lays out the clients' argument and rationale for the project. It states:

- to whom the strategic brief is addressed and what is requested of them
- how the project relates to its role or mission statement, its objectives and business plan
- the context – why the project is necessary and what current problems it will solve
- what broadly will be provided and how it will support activities
- size and costs – both capital and operating, whole-life costing
- the business case for the project
- programme and milestone dates
- quality requirements of the new space – materials, durability and maintenance
- environmental objectives
- statutory compliance implications

The exercise will probably be carried out by the clients and their financial advisors. It aims to ensure that the project is financially prudent, and to establish financial management over it. It is designed to achieve approval from top management and funding agencies to continue to the next stage of the project. If it has not been completed when the briefing consultant is appointed, the consultant may well be required to assist with it. For large and publicly funded projects approval of the strategic brief is a key gateway through which the project must pass towards approval of funding.

2.1.4 Project brief

Once the strategic brief has been approved, subject to any necessary amendment, work can start on the project brief. This is addressed to the design team; it sets down the requirements that the design is to satisfy. Again, for all but the smallest projects, it will probably be carried out in several phases as the design is developed. It is discussed further in the second section of this chapter, and in detailed checklists in Chapters 10 and 11. The project brief is the 'bible' against which the design is assessed until the completion of production information. It may also form the basis of requirements for specialist consultants and subcontractors in some non-traditional procurement paths.

2.1.5 Post-project evaluation

Post-project evaluation occurs once construction is complete and the space has been commissioned and occupied by the users for several months. It should not happen until the users have had time to settle into the new building, and have recovered from the disruption of the move. It is particularly relevant for large projects, for publicly funded projects, and for those that form part of a larger, ongoing building programme. Questions are asked in three categories:

- How successful was the process of briefing and design, and what lessons can be learnt?
  How well did the various participants perform?
  How effective was communication between them?
  This review is unlikely to be successful unless it is carried out in a collaborative, non-blaming way. If the review is tied to questions of liability, it is unlikely that anyone will wish to participate.

- Does the building meet the objectives and requirements stated in the briefing documents, both as an object in space and in terms of the operation of its various systems?
  This is a technical review of the building against objectives, requirements and benchmarks, and may well be carried out by the briefing consultant or – perhaps better – by an independent consultant with no previous involvement. It may include a technical review of the performance of services systems and an analysis of their costs in use in the first year.

- How satisfied are the clients and building users with the new space? Does it work well for them?
  Here post-occupancy evaluation techniques are similar to the survey techniques described in Chapter 6.[2]

2.2 Briefing and design

The previous section looked at briefing in the context of procurement decisions, and the clients' financial management of the project. This section looks at how the brief supports the design team, again in terms of the sequence of events.[3] The sequence is shown in Figure 2.1. The activities of briefing are shown in three columns representing tasks relating to client, briefing and design.

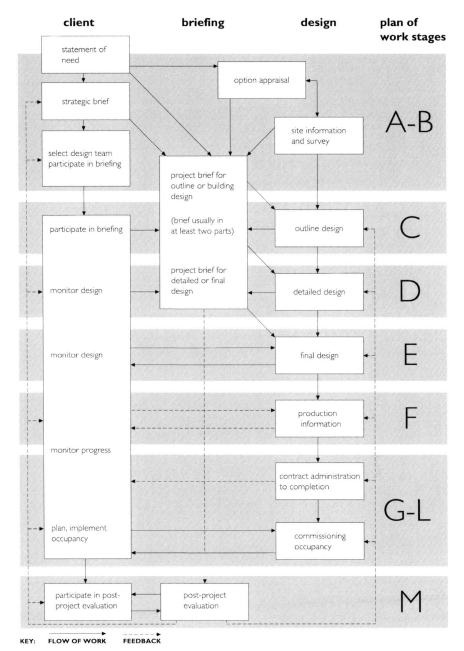

client	briefing	design	plan of work stages

statement of need

option appraisal

strategic brief

site information and survey

A-B

select design team participate in briefing

project brief for outline or building design

participate in briefing

(brief usually in at least two parts)

outline design

C

project brief for detailed or final design

monitor design

detailed design

D

monitor design

final design

E

production information

F

monitor progress

contract administration to completion

G-L

plan, implement occupancy

commissioning occupancy

participate in post-project evaluation

post-project evaluation

M

KEY: FLOW OF WORK   FEEDBACK

Figure 2.1 Briefing and design

The project starts when a need for space is identified and defined. This is the *statement of need*, usually conducted by the clients without professional advice. It is quite possible for clients to carry out an option appraisal and certainly to write a strategic brief without assistance from property professionals, but the sooner professional advice is sought, the better for the project. The clients need to have sufficient understanding of their needs and options to select and instruct a design team, and a briefing consultant is well placed to help them with that process. Alternatively, the briefing consultant may join the project with the design team. At this point, it may be necessary to help the clients retrace a few steps to catch up with any tasks that have been missed.

Early on in the process, a *site survey* will be necessary[4] along with collection of information about such things as planning requirements, legal constraints, utilities, and access. These activities are not properly part of briefing, but they influence it, and can be carried out either by the design architect or by the briefing consultant.

The *project brief* itself will usually be produced as two documents: a brief for building design, and a brief for detailed design. Checklists of questions to be asked in compiling these are to be found in Chapters 10 and 11 respectively. As well as the formal documentation of briefing information, approved by the clients, in many situations there will be a continuous conversation between the briefing consultant (defining the requirements) and the design architect (proposing solutions that meet them). The design architect will of course be integrating form, function, cost, structure, technology, site, aesthetics, statutory regulations and a host of other things, while the briefing consultant will focus on client and user requirements.

Note also that in Figure 2.1 decisions made in earlier steps inform and constrain decisions in subsequent stages during the development of the project.

Briefing should be complete before the final design stage. Changes inevitably occur during design development, and it is advisable to have an agreed formal procedure for clients to authorise variations from the approved brief. In some circumstances it may be wise for clients to have the briefing consultant assess the final design for conformity to the approved brief and variations, and to carry out a similar check on production information.

Following occupancy, *post-project evaluation* as described above provides an opportunity for all parties to benefit in future projects from lessons learnt.

2.3 Levels of scale

More complex projects often move through a series of levels of scale from larger scale to smaller, though few projects start at the largest and proceed continuously to the smallest scale. As already noted, decisions made at the higher level become con-straints at the more detailed level. It is more important to recognise the levels of scale that exist than to look for fixed definitions of the boundaries between them. Table 2.2 shows a series of descriptions in which a briefing document is produced at each level of scale.

Table 2.2 Levels of project scale

Scale	Brief	Design
region	service plan	property strategy and action plan
campus	campus development plan	campus master plan
single building	project brief for building design	building design
fitting out	project brief for detailed design	detailed design and fitting out
furniture	brief for a piece of furniture	design for a piece of furniture

In this table, the word *campus* is used to describe any group of related buildings; they need not necessarily be academic. It may be used, for instance, for a large hospital, or for a collection of city office blocks occupied by a single company and within easy walking distance.

Occasionally there are specific items at the detailed scale that need to be pulled out and dealt with early on. Consider, for example, a library, for which the designer wishes to express the shape of individual study carrels on the exterior of the building. Briefing for the carrel component could be pulled out and defined in the brief for outline design rather than in the brief for detailed design. Another example might be a group of buildings in which some spaces require air conditioning but the majority do not. This issue might be addressed at the campus level rather than at the single building level so that buildings can be grouped to allow efficient common servicing.

The term *furniture* in Table 2.2 can apply equally to all sort of components and systems within the building, including windows, cladding, equipment, finishes, signage, lighting, information technology, and communications. At this level, the role statement will describe the function of the component, whereas in the preceding levels it described the role of the user organisation. At the component level briefing takes the form of a performance specification.

Sequencing in this way simplifies the management of information and communications within the procurement team. It permits, for instance, the design and construction of the shell and core of a large building while briefing and design for fitting out are left until the information is actually required.

1   This figure and the text that follows are based on Construction Industry Board booklet, F. Duffy (ed.), *Briefing The Team*, Thomas Telford, London, 1997.
2   See also W. Preiser et al. *Post Occupancy Evaluation*, Van Nostrand Reinhold, New York, 1987.
3   For further reading see S. Lupton, ed. *Architect's Job Book* Seventh Edition, RIBA Publications, 2000, on which this section and Figure 2.1 are based.
4   Site surveys are covered in detail in David Hughes, Raymond Gilfillen and Mike O'Reilly, *Construction Companion to Site Investigations*, RIBA Publications, London (forthcoming).

3 Briefing as a process

Chapter 1 examined *what* briefing is – the logic of the briefing process – and described a six-step process that, in principle, applies to briefing of most types and sizes. Chapter 2 looked at *when* it should occur – the timing of briefing within the design process and its relationship to procurement decisions. This chapter begins the description of the process from a practical point of view – *how* briefing is done. This description continues in some detail throughout the remainder of the book, but it starts by going step by step through a typical briefing process from the practical viewpoint of the briefing consultant.

Whatever the stage in the process of procurement, briefing is essentially a very similar process, which is reiterated in greater detail at each subsequent stage. The steps are:

1 defining the briefing project
2 information gathering
3 decision-making
4 documenting
5 testing
6 amendments and approval

3.1 Defining the briefing project

3.1.1 Getting started

At the outset, the briefing consultant defines the service to be provided in the briefing process. It is usual for the brief writer to submit a proposal for this task, along with a fee quotation and a time programme.

Clients often commence construction projects in some degree of disarray, unless they are experienced, and even then the quality of decision-making that has made them successful in other spheres may somehow be left behind when they are facing the prospect of new space. Construction projects tend to start with a pile of unresolved issues, without a clear way forward, and with the clients unsure as to how to tackle the problem. The answer is to call in professional help.

From the consultant's point of view it is important to keep the briefing process separate from the process of securing a commission for the full architectural service. If the architect is selected on the basis of a design presentation, assumptions will be made about the brief without taking time to find out what in fact is required. The clients may be under the misapprehension that because a practice has designed a number of schools, restaurants or offices, it will immediately know what is required for their particular school, restaurant or office. Each has shared similarities, but each is fundamentally a unique set of circumstances, which briefing articulates. The consultant needs to make briefing a selling point. Depending on the experience and competence of the clients, it is important that the consultant takes the time to have distinct conversations with them outside the briefing process itself, in order to:

- explain that it is more cost-effective to take the time to get the brief right now than to alter mistakes in the building later
- explain to the clients when existing briefing notes are inadequate
- negotiate separately on fees for the subsequent design work
- deal with the clients' concerns about the programme
- deal with the clients' concerns about the cost of a briefing exercise
- compete with other building professionals for a place on the team
- define terms of reference and fees for the briefing exercise, to be presented as a proposal

There are no easy answers. It is essential to be clear about what needs to be done and why, and to avoid being confused by the conflicting aims of clients or colleagues.

3.1.2 Initial walk-around survey

Where there are existing buildings and operations, the project commences with an initial walk-around survey. Taken during the preparation of the proposal, it allows an impression to be formed of the quality and suitability of existing buildings, of how well they are currently being used, and of the activities performed by staff. An assessment can be made of the types of detailed survey that will be required during the briefing project. A trained observer will bring a fresh eye, which will develop a sense of the culture of the organisation from the way it inhabits space. Client representatives can point out problems as they see them, on the ground.

The consultant needs to ask questions, take notes, and take photographs. It is useful to note photograph positions on plans as reminders of each area or to illustrate problems.

3.1.3 Proposal

It has been said that, in order to write a proposal for a briefing project, one has more or less to do the project. To understand the project sufficiently clearly to decide what needs to be done, one needs to go lightly over all the areas that will be undertaken later in detail.

The best key to understanding the project is to understand the various areas that set its context. These typically are:

- the business context – why the project is required and financially viable
- the management context – what key management issues need solutions
- the facilities strategy – following from the business plan, how the project sits within an overall strategy for property and facilities
- existing operations – what people do in the clients' various departments
- existing buildings and sites or approved designs
- potential new sites

A substantial part of the project may involve leading the clients to a clearer understanding of the policy, management, and operational issues of how the new space will be used. There are companies now that come to a briefing project with a clear understanding of these issues, but they are rare. It is rarer still for top management to be completely in agreement on key issues.

It is also important to understand the parameters or edges of the project and its relationship to other possible projects, current or planned. This is the time to take a step back from the scope of the project that the client has defined, to check whether taking a view of the bigger picture opens opportunities that should definitely be investigated. This may well result in better solutions if done consciously and in collaboration with the client. It is important to be clear about the value and cost-effectiveness to the client of any extra briefing work that may require additional fees.

3.1.4 Defining the tasks

Each piece of work required to complete the briefing project is listed. This involves looking ahead to the final product – the report, drawings, workshop or presentation – and working backwards to the present. The first question to ask is 'What's the package?' – what is the set of deliverables to be handed over or carried out in order to complete the project? A project must not be contracted for a fixed fee unless the package of deliverables is clearly defined. If the project is open ended, so too should be the fee. On a large project it may be reasonable to enter into a contract for a preliminary exploratory exercise of fixed duration in order to define the scope of the main briefing exercise that will follow. A contract for briefing work must not be entered into until the end is established as realisable.

It only remains to write and submit the proposal. A checklist for writing a proposal is given in Chapter 12.

3.2 Information gathering

Finding the information to inform a brief is not usually a problem. As in any research project, the skill lies in selecting key relevant information from the rest and in assessing the place of each set of information. To avoid being overwhelmed by the sheer quantity of information that a large organisation will provide, it needs to be assessed on arrival and filed by the briefing task for which it is required. Ideally, information received is assessed and slotted into its place in the brief document as the work progresses. Apart from relevance, information is also assessed for accuracy and integrity.

3.2.1 Categories of information

In assessing what to do with information gathered, the first step is to sort it into the following categories:

- comparable buildings, standards, benchmarks
- comparable organisations, their operations and technological change
- organisational strategy and policy, or the business plan
- management, the organisation of staff and operations
- facilities strategies, plans and policies, including standards
- operations or activities – what staff and visitors do and how it is done
- existing or new sites – their size, characteristics and suitability
- existing or new buildings – their size, characteristics and suitability

3.2.2 Sources of information

Information will come from a number of sources:

- the clients' own documents
- interviews, meetings and workshops with management, building users (sometimes, for especially sensitive developments, workshops or meetings with local residents or the public are necessary)
- books and periodicals describing briefing requirements and design solutions for similar buildings[1]
- books and periodicals describing issues, trends and new technology in the clients' industry sector
- visits organised to comparable buildings, or telephone interviews with their managers (people are often prepared to give a little time on the phone if they receive in return a short research report in which anonymous data from say a dozen facilities are compared)

- surveys of existing or possible buildings
- surveys to understand operations and use of space in existing operations
- surveys of staff attitudes and opinions
- work with focus groups

Surveys, and how to conduct them, are discussed in Chapter 6.

3.3 Decision-making

3.3.1 Roles in decision-making

The client group takes decisions. The role of the briefing consultant is to organise and lead the decision-making process. The consultant is expert in assisting clients to make decisions, but doesn't actually make them. Chapter 6 contains descriptions of techniques for achieving decisions, should the clients have difficulties. If all else fails, it is reasonable to make strong recommendations, stopping short of actually deciding. The consultant's role is to identify, formulate and present the issues that require resolution. This involves sorting and ordering the data needed to inform and support decisions. The client group may well be unable to isolate and articulate the issues clearly themselves, lacking the perspective and experience of an external consultant. Bringing order to a problem that appears insoluble is often the briefing consultant's most important contribution. For an architect, trained to make quick assessments and decisions, the role of consultant may require some adjustment of attitude.

3.3.2 Issues, options and implications

An issue is a situation demanding resolution. Resolution is only possible once the problem has been defined. For each issue, two or three options or ways ahead can usually be identified and described. There are rarely more than three options, though there may be detailed variations of a basic option. Each option will inherently include the implications of following that route. There will always be a cost implication, a quality implication and often a time implication. Implications can be compared for feasibility, convenience, risk, initial cost, cost in use, impact on operations, and programme, among others. Options should be tested against the objectives within the role statement, and against activity descriptions.

Discussion of options may well raise management and operational issues that will have implications for physical design solutions. The consultant should be prepared consciously to revisit the role statement and activity description if necessary.

3.3.3 Issue categories and the limitations of design

Clients often need assistance in distinguishing between management or policy issues, operational issues and facility issues, as they often arise together in discussion. Management or policy issues relate to the overall intention, organisation and direction of the organisation. Operational issues relate to how things are done on a day-to-day basis. Issues in these areas need to be resolved by the organisation. The briefing consultant can identify and define them, and options can be proposed, but ultimately they must be decided by management. Design alone cannot solve management or operational problems; only managers and staff can do that. The idea that buildings somehow determine how people will behave is a fallacy. Buildings either hinder or facilitate activities. Consciously or not, building design will symbolise values. Buildings can create an image sympathetic to particular principles and ideals. Buildings can encourage or discourage particular behaviour but, apart from solid walls, strong locks, good lighting and visibility, buildings cannot produce or prevent particular behaviour. For instance, it is not uncommon to hear people speak of a 'democratic building'. What they mean is a building that symbolises democratic ideals, or possibly a building that does not symbolise hierarchies and in which communication is convenient, or a building that is accessible and visible to the passing public. It is important to be clear as to what is actually meant. Buildings are not democratic; they do not vote or take part in decision-making by representatives.

3.3.4 Participation in briefing

There are generally two groups of participants in the briefing process: those involved with policy, funding and management of the construction project overall, and those who understand the buiding users' detailed needs. There may of course be some overlap between the two groups. There is an essential difference of attitude between those who focus on getting the project built and those who aim to support user activities. Both are needed, but the second group must be allowed to arrive at conclusions in the brief before the rush to design and implementation starts. It is definitely preferable, for similar reasons, that the briefing consultant is not the same person as the design architect, but this may be feasible only in larger architects' offices. The briefing consultant will champion the client and building users; the design architect will naturally be concerned for a design that reconciles the many technical, statutory, site and aesthetic objectives – in which user requirements may not be a high priority.

3.3.5 Who should be involved?

On a very small project, the client may be represented by only one or two people. On slightly larger projects, a single client briefing group will take all decisions. This will ideally consist of:

- the clients' project coordinator, who will be the primary day-to-day contact between the client organisation and the briefing consultant
- the clients' project sponsor, a senior manager, who will champion the project within the client organisation, overcoming barriers to progress and creating an understanding of the case for the project
- one or more department heads
- the facilities manager
- staff representatives or technical personnel with knowledge of key processes

On a larger project it is best to set up two bodies: a high-level steering committee that meets at the beginning, middle and end of the project, and a working group that meets regularly throughout the project.

The *steering committee* consists of:

- the project sponsor
- the senior management decision-maker, with power to sanction funding
- any professional advisors

It authorises the project, follows progress from a distance, is available to provide decisions on strategic issues, and approves the final brief document.

The *working group* deals with the vast majority of decisions, and deals with the detail. It consists of:

- the project sponsor
- the clients' project coordinator
- building user representatives
- one or more department heads

In addition, and depending on the procurement process, there may also be others, such as the project manager, the prime contractor, the facilities manager, a property consultant and the developer.

One of the purposes of the steering committee is to avoid the situation where a brief is produced that is then sent for approval by an individual or group that has not been party to the decision-making process. The briefing process is educational for everyone involved, and bad decisions arise when those with authority have not worked through it and do not feel that they 'own' the results. Typical is the distant finance director, who approves a brief unread, subject to a cost reduction of 15%, without understanding the corresponding reduction in scope and quality. Cost reductions may well be necessary, but there are always implications.

The composition of the working group and the amount of participation by building users will depend on the management culture of the client organisation. The people selected to sit on briefing teams are representative of the organisation as a whole, and much of their value is as representatives. Many of them, including key figures, will almost certainly not be involved with the organisation by the time the new space is occupied. The decisions they take in briefing will bind their successors, and one role of the consultant is to ensure that the brief reflects broadly accepted opinion and best practice.

In addition to the formal membership of working groups, one can learn a great deal by striking up conversations with people who may not have high status in the organisation but who know a great deal about what actually goes on. People such as porters, technicians, counter staff and secretaries can give valuable insights into crucial workings. Some organisations have a culture that is sufficiently non-hierarchical to recognise and draw on the insights of such people, and may include them in working groups, but in Britain this is quite rare.

Once the membership of committees has been agreed, it is usual for the consultant to send a letter to participants introducing the project and the briefing exercise, and explaining what is required of participants. If a series of two, three or more meetings can be scheduled at that point, this will help participants plan their time commitment to the process. On smaller projects, this can be done verbally and with less formality.

3.4 Documenting

3.4.1 Organising the material

Writing the brief begins after the first meeting. Details of the decisions will not be known, but the format is clearly foreseeable, and typical contents are given below. Decisions reached are documented in a chapter of the draft brief for review at the next meeting. If it has been agreed to produce an overhead or computer presentation, the key points of each chapter of the draft brief should be presented in that format, backed up by additional detailed text and tables for reference if required.

Writing the draft brief is a matter of synthesising the information gathered, and presenting it in a format that is easy for the design team to access. There is a natural tendency, when writing, to describe the process of information gathering and decision-making in the order in which it occurred. This is not what the design team needs to know, and should be avoided.

Chapter 12 contains a checklist for a typical brief contents list around which most briefing documents could be organised.

3.4.2 What to leave out

Briefing is as much about what is not written as about what is. As already noted, the obvious can be left out. There should be a confidence in the basic competence of the design team. Everyone's time can be saved by not mentioning things that are conventionally accepted good practice. The focus must be on clarifying choices, and on the unexpected. The exception to this is where the brief will form part of contract documentation. In this case it may be necessary to specify far more: to state that the job should be well done, and to define precisely what is meant by 'well done' in this context.

A brief can be used by a client or project manager to limit design options in certain areas, to ensure consistency through a number of projects, or to keep the design team on track. These approaches are reasonable, within limits. Apart from such explicit requirements, it is better to write a brief that allows as many unforeseen design solutions as possible. This imposes a certain tact on the briefing consultant, in refraining from defining the problem in such detail that only a narrow range of solutions is possible.

3.5 Testing

As the draft brief is compiled, and again once it is completed, it is tested in the areas described below. There may initially be several basic options to test using the criteria set out in the brief, such as extending space on an existing site, leasing additional space, or acquiring a new building or site. It is a matter of finding a fit between demand, expressed as the brief requirements, and supply, represented by possible sites or buildings. Using the logical route through defining role, activities, and requirements, the impact of each option on organisational policy, objectives and operations is assessed. A detailed checklist for testing is given in Chapter 12. Its main headings are:

- accuracy and consistency
- fit
- budget
- business case
- programme
- technical feasibility
- impacts
- procurement route
- statutory compliance
- resources
- commitment

Perhaps the last heading, *commitment*, is the most important. If the design team produces a building that meets the requirements documented in this brief, does the client group really like it and want it? Are they committed to go ahead with the project as described in the brief? Would it meet the needs of this client group and the needs of those who will succeed them?

3.6 Amendment and approval

At this stage the draft brief has been presented to the client group, and time has been allowed for review. Copies are returned, marked up with comments. If the process has been thorough, amendments should be minor and there should be no late surprises. A meeting is required to report back following the testing stage. The selection of options should have been greatly clarified. There may be minor issues to be resolved. Once this is done, the brief is amended and circulated. A presentation based on the final document may be required, probably for the benefit of those not immediately involved in the process.

Ultimately a decision is required: to proceed to design on the basis of the brief or not. This decision needs to be confirmed in writing. In some situations, a formal signing-off sheet is appropriate. Signing off marks the end of the briefing process. Where briefing is sequenced in a number of passes of increasing detail, it marks the end of that phase.

Nothing stands still. As the project is taken forward into design and construction, requirements may change. If the client is a large organisation, a procedure for considering and authorising amendments to the final brief is advisable. The procedure will identify the proposed change, reasons, assessment of options, costs and benefits, design implications, implications for the construction programme, and budget. It will be tested against all of the criteria described in the testing section. The amendment will be incorporated only after consideration and approval by top management.

From the viewpoint of the briefing consultant it is important to keep focused on completing the service described in the proposal. This generally ends with the distribution of the final brief document.

Discipline is required to complete a project. There is a tendency to continue tying up the inevitable minor loose ends when really the project is done. Any additional consultancy work should be described and authorised separately. Successfully completing a briefing exercise requires considerably more skill than starting one.

3.7 Process and product

This chapter has taken an overview of briefing as a process from the viewpoint of what the consultant does. The aim is to produce a product – a document – but in so doing the client group is led through a decision-making process that in many ways is as valuable to the client as the document that is finally produced. The brief document as a product is structured for easy access by the design team. It contains the information they need, presented in a comprehensible order. At the same time it is the record and culmination of the decision-making process that brought it about. Without the consultative process the brief is merely the view of an external consultant, however expert. With it, the client groups gain a sense of ownership and commitment that only comes through participation. They have wrestled with the issues and understood the implications; they have been party to the trade-offs, and can justify the decisions and the assumptions on which they were based. If decisions are questioned later, the brief stands as evidence that they were taken prudently as a result of careful consideration. The protection this affords to individual participants is often appreciated, particularly in publicly funded organisations. Perhaps more important, the briefing process brings users and management together to reconsider their objectives and the design of operations, so that the new space will truly support their activities. The briefing process potentially contains elements of organisational development, team building and education. It ties the clients' business plan to a description of space that specifically supports it. The process is at least as important as the product.

1 Search the RIBA Online Catalogue at www.architecture.com

For further reading on briefing as a process, one of the better recent books is Donna Duerk, *Architectural Programming, Information Management for Design*, John Wiley, New York, 1993. It is also excellent on briefing technique and particularly on research methodology. It is written for an American readership but contains much that would be useful for British architects.

4 Players and roles

The various players in the briefing process have distinct approaches and perspectives. This chapter discusses some of those viewpoints. They deserve consideration, because they will be represented in some form in any briefing process, whether or not by individuals sitting around the table.

As procurement routes for buildings change, the briefing consultant will work under a variety of contractual situations. The employer may change; the commercial context for briefing may change; but the basic briefing process will remain very much constant and, with it, the roles explored in this chapter:

- clients
- building users
- developer
- facilities manager
- project manager
- design team
- public interest
- briefing consultant

4.1 Clients

4.1.1 The ideal clients

Rarely do briefing consultants have a great deal of choice over their clients. They may target certain building types and client categories, but projects generally choose consultants and not the other way round. What makes an ideal client? Given a briefing consultant who asks the right questions and guides the process expertly, a client blessed with competent business management skills and a willingness to devote time and energy consistently throughout the project goes a long way towards meeting the ideal.

4.1.2 Client size

The larger and more complex the project, the greater the time commitment and competence required. Large clients with large projects and a rolling construction programme will generally have property professionals acting as professional clients. Smaller client organisations usually, but not always, have smaller projects, and are possibly inexperienced in construction projects. This need not be a drawback if the clients have time, commitment and good management skills, and are prepared to make timely decisions and stick to them.

4.1.3 Client skills

The skills needed in a client are:

- a clear understanding of the overall mission and strategy of the organisation
- the ability to draw on the skills of others within the organisation, delegating and using an in-house project coordinator
- good communication within the organisation and with consultants
- the ability to work with budgets, and to understand value and risk
- the ability to know and accept when a good decision has been achieved.[1]

If these factors are missing in any way, then the consultant will need to compensate with additional skill, time and encouragement. Ultimately, the brief is only as good as the skill and effort that both clients and consultant bring to it.

The government is aware of these issues, and has defined client roles and the skills required of those who fill them.[2] They are equally applicable to private sector projects. Some of those skills are:

- decisiveness – the ability to make decisions and be accountable for them
- challenging – a questioning attitude in testing proposals
- communication – establishing good lines of communication and having good listening skills
- technical skills – competence or, depending on the role, at least understanding in a range of technical areas relating to investment and construction

4.1.4 Clients and budgets

Clients begin the procurement process with one of three questions:

- How much space can we get for this fixed sum?
- How much will space cost that meets these requirements?
- How much will space cost that meets our requirements, which haven't yet been defined?[3]

The briefing process will answer these questions with increasing degrees of precision, but it is important to understand the budgetary context of the briefing exercise. It is also important to know from the start that realistic funds are available to back the clients' objectives and intentions.

Table 4.1 Understanding of briefing, dimensions of client type

	less	**understanding of briefing**			**more**
Client experience	naïve, first-time client	business-like first-time client	occasional client	experienced client, frequent projects	professional client, large construction programme
Client commitment and competence	poor commitment, poor decision-making	willing but disorganised	well organised but sporadic commitment	competent and committed	experienced, committed competent professional
	smaller	**project size**			**larger**

4.1.5 Client categories

As a summary, Table 4.1 shows clients categorised by experience, commitment and competence. There is often, but not necessarily, an approximate coincidence between these factors and project size.

Looking at the project itself, a key factor is how well a building type has been understood and documented. Most building types have been extensively researched, described and illustrated. In these cases, the brief can consist of a list of floor areas and notes on where requirements differ from what is normally expected in buildings of the relevant type. At the other end of the spectrum there are one-off buildings for new purposes, and those for which few examples exist for comparison. These benefit from a more extensive briefing exercise, and from greater client experience and expertise.

A further factor is project size. Complexity usually increases with building size and the number of building users. In any case, the larger the user organisation, the greater the savings to be made by getting briefing right. Small area savings over a large building create substantial cost savings. Though it is harder to prove, the same is true of small productivity improvements in a large workforce.[4]

Table 4.2 indicates the need for detailed briefing in relation to project size and published knowledge about building type, though there is not necessarily a direct linear relationship between them.

Table 4.2 Requirement for briefing, dimensions of project type

	less	**Detailed briefing and client experience**			**more**
Project size	under £250k	over £250k	over £1m	over £10m	over £100m
Building users	under 25 users	over 25 users	over 100 users	over 1000 users	over 5000 users
Understood building type	well understood, documented	understood but requires major rethink	traditional, poorly documented	new type, few precedents	completely unprecedented

4.1.6 Process expertise and building type expertise

The skills of a briefing consultant are transferable between building types. If the process is good, the particular issues of an individual project and building type will be easy to deal with. The consultant is aware of this, but the client may well not be. Clients want to engage a consultant with experience and proven success in their particular building type. This is quite understandable from the clients' perspective but not very helpful to the consultant, experienced in the briefing process.

In the extreme, the client looks to the consultant as an expert not in process but in building type. Seen this way, the consultant's task is to tell the clients what is good for their organisation. There is an analogy here with medicine. There was a time when one looked to a doctor to prescribe the pills that would cure the illness: ask no questions, take the pills, and one gets better.

Modern doctors sit the patient down for a conversation about their problems and lifestyle, after which a treatment plan is developed, in which the patient participates in making choices and taking responsibility for actions that will improve health and welfare. Of course, there has to be the expertise to prescribe the right pills, but that is far from the whole story.

It is reasonable to discuss with the clients which of these two approaches they expect, and whether their expectations are consistent with the service that the consultant has to offer. It is important to avoid misunderstandings in this area before a project commences. Some knowledge of building type can be an advantage: 'not reinventing the wheel'. Refining solutions over a series of projects can be an advantage; recycling outdated solutions is clearly a disadvantage. Ideally, most clients will welcome a fresh look at their particular problem, backed by the experience of others that were similar.

4.2 Building users

Building users are of two types: employees and volunteers. Employees of the client organisation are given the task of participation in briefing, whereas volunteers are relatively unconnected users. They may be passengers in an airport, patients in a hospital, shoppers in a department store, primary schoolchildren, or local residents. Both employees and volunteers are important, but their motivation and availability will be different. If invited to participate in the briefing process, volunteers are giving their time as a favour to answer a questionnaire, or to attend focus group sessions. The ideal volunteer is willing, articulate, and a typical representative of a recognised category of building user.

These requirements apply equally to employee participants in briefing. The ideal qualities are commitment, basic organisational competence, and a detailed knowledge of operations. If the project is large and the time commitment substantial, they will be anxious about the effect of their absence from their normal job. In large organisations useful information is gathered by surveys and focus groups, which can be less obtrusive and less time consuming.

4.3 Developer

4.3.1 The developer's perspective

Whether the space is for private or commercial use, there is always a developer figure in the picture. Whether the client is developing space for their own use or to let or sell, whoever assumes the risk of investing in the project will also be expecting a return on that investment. The difference is that the commercial developer expects a greater return than an owner-occupier. Any client, commercial or otherwise, is looking for a return that is relatively certain and which will at least equal alternative investments. In addition, the commercial developer expects a return for creating value, for taking risk, and for managing the project. The developer needs construction professionals who work reliably to budget and to programme in order to limit risk. Relatively small unexpected increases in time or cost can threaten a project's overall viability. Time is critical because of the costs of borrowing, which start with the purchase of the site and decrease only when the completed space is let or sold.

4.3.2 Quality versus cost

As in any industry, there is a choice between high quality and high cost, and their opposites. Some developments follow tried and tested formulae in brief and design in order to produce a lower-cost product of average quality. In this case the brief will largely address commercial and site requirements.

Example
A developer of office buildings has calculated that external cladding is one of the most expensive elements of a building. A design guideline in his standard brief gives a ratio between floor area and area of external wall that results in large floor plates and simple planar façades. It also gives a percentage for openings. Another developer, concerned that the majority of users have good access to natural light, specifies a percentage of the floor area that must be within 7 m of windows.

Other developers aim at a sophisticated specialised market, which will pay a premium for high-quality space resulting from a well-researched brief. This market requires a brief that addresses user requirements as well as meeting the developer's commercial requirements. Producing a brief of this sort for a developer is an exercise in market research, and brings a degree of certainty to what started as the developer's hunch. It results in a detailed understanding of the target market, which is used both to provide space that meets users' needs and to market the finished product. The issues to be resolved are similar to those where the user is the client, though there will be changes in emphasis.

Finally, there is what has been called the 'triple whammy' of user satisfaction, environmental sustainability, and a high return on investment, albeit over the longer term.[5] It is certainly possible to achieve this, but not without an intentional effort, and that starts with the brief.

4.3.3 Lending institutions

Behind every developer is what a lending institution, which is as interested in the security of its investment as the developer. A good brief and strong project management should help to convince lenders that the project will create value by meeting real needs.

It is important to understand developers' objectives and the pressures they are under. It also helps to have some understanding of developers' calculations, and to use them to test and justify briefing recommendations.

4.4 Facilities manager

For the design architect, the project is complete when the users occupy it. Barring a few details, when the users move in, the architects' work is done. That is when the facilities manager takes over running the building on a day-to-day basis, though he or she will probably have already been involved in commissioning and move management, if not also in briefing and design. The facilities manager should have a database on how an existing building functions.[6] This will include the historic costs of minor alterations and repairs to the fabric as well as the maintenance and operating costs of mechanical and electrical services. In large organisations the facilities manager will also have data on cleaning, catering, security and similar building services.

Whatever the size of the client, someone will be filling this role with a greater or lesser degree of professionalism. In larger organisations they may be called premises manager, accommodation manager or facilities manager. In smaller organisations the role may be performed by a general manager, office manager, finance manager, maintenance manager, housekeeper or maybe home maker.

The facilities manager is a valuable ally in briefing because of his or her detailed knowledge of the relationship between an organisation's operations and the space it occupies. There should also be an understanding of the value of physical resources in relation to productivity and the business plan. There will certainly be a concern for approaches that work at an operational level, ease of maintenance, ease of cleaning, and the durability of components and finishes. There may well be quantified benchmarks for the performance of finishes, components and services. In many buildings, adaptability of space and ease of internal reorganisation or external expansion are also issues. The facilities manager basically wants a building that is low on operating costs, more than adequate in facilities provided, and all within an affordable and predictable budget.

It is often appropriate for the facilities manager to act as the clients' project coordinator for the briefing exercise. He or she is in a good position to manage the flow of information between the briefing consultant and departmental heads or other user representatives. On larger projects, coordination is a full-time commitment, and may require a small team.

4.5 Project manager

4.5.1 Time constraints

Whereas briefing is about defining requirements, project management is concerned with realisation on the ground, and with contract completion, though it may not necessarily be formally responsible for contract administration.[7] This immediately introduces a potential tension between the project manager and the briefing consultant on the issue of time. Briefing is about stepping back from the rush to completion and looking dispassionately and thoroughly at requirements. To a project manager, who may be under great pressure to have space ready for occupancy as soon as possible, the time taken by briefing may appear unnecessarily leisurely. Briefing is only justified because it increases the probability of creating space that meets real needs. This reduces the risk of expensive changes during design or, worse, during construction. However, it takes time to organise and weigh the evidence and come to decisions in a briefing process, and the project manager may need to be convinced that the time taken is cost-effective and well spent.

4.5.2 Scope, cost and time

The project manager has three variables to balance: cost, time and scope, with scope including both quality and extent. The three are closely linked: any change in one will affect the other two. Briefing is primarily concerned with defining scope, and with testing that definition against time and cost. Alternatively, it can define scope within fixed limits of cost and time.

4.6 The design team

We have drawn a distinction between defining a problem during briefing and solving it through design. From this perspective the design team has no place in briefing. In practice the line between the two processes is blurred, and there are a number of places where the design team can contribute to briefing.

First, and most obviously, where briefing is sequenced over time in a number of passes of increasing detail, an approved design at the less detailed level becomes a fixed constraint at the more detailed level. For example, a master plan for a university campus becomes a constraint on subsequent briefing for a single building on the campus.

Site analysis lies somewhere between briefing and design. A site is both a fixed constraint in briefing and a stimulus for developing design. Whether the task of site analysis is done by design architect or by briefing consultant matters less than the fact that the information is available to both when required. Similarly, feasibility studies are a necessary part of testing a brief, and can be carried out by either team. Feasibility may depend on potential capacities of existing buildings, and engineers may be asked to carry out specialist investigations into services infrastructure, structural capacity, and similar technical areas.

In all of this it is essential to ensure that the emerging design does not pre-empt the brief, but that the brief springs from an analysis of needs and not from the design. For this reason it has been recommended that the design team are not members of the briefing team, though they may be consulted from time to time.

4.7 Public interest

The legislative framework that includes planning control, building regulations and health and safety legislation provides another context for briefing, design and construction. The public interest always has a presence at the briefing process, and the draft brief is tested for compliance with the legislation. A building will probably outlast the involvement of any of the participants in its construction, and there is a duty to future generations to use the planet's precious limited resources to build something that will generate minimum pollution and provide a healthy, serviceable environment over time.

There are also those sensitive projects for which it is either required or advisable to consult the public directly or through users' and residents' organisations. It may be better to commence consultation at the briefing stage, rather than later when elements of the design are fixed. The organisation and nature of consultation will vary with the project. The consultation process may be resented by the design team as an imposition or, alternatively, seen as an opportunity to listen to the needs of local people and learn from their insights and experience.

There are situations where clients wish to go beyond the requirements of legislation, to do and be seen to do the right thing. There seems to be increased concern for ethics in business, and nowhere does this appear more clearly than in concern for the environment. This concern has crystallised into two concepts: the awareness that the level of material comfort enjoyed in the West today is in many ways bought at the expense of the populations of poorer parts of the world, and the idea that it should not be at the expense of scarcity in future generations. These ideas are discussed in greater detail in Chapter 5. It is sufficient to note here that the public interest is global and inter-generational. Whether silent or expressed, it is present at the meeting table whenever briefing for any project is discussed, and the brief is the best point in a project to commence effective action.

4.8 The briefing consultant

What does one look for in a briefing consultant? First, a view that understands the needs of clients and users on the one hand and of designers and the building industry on the other. The consultant is the interpreter between the two groups. Next, an understanding of business, its motivations and ways of expression. Even if the project is a family house, the capital sums involved usually imply major investment decisions for the family, which will have effects for many years. An ability to think strategically is essential – to see the big picture, to find ways through seemingly intractable problems. Along with this go skills in presentation and negotiation. It also calls for the architect's traditional skill of creative problem-solving, applied in a different way.

Perhaps the most important skill for the consultant is the ability to listen: not only to hear what is being said accurately, but to listen for the feelings that lie behind what is said, and for what is not being said. People often feel they have not been listened to as designers rush on with their project.

An enquiring mind is required: one that probes and tests ideas and technical problems, and one that is not afraid to ask the simple obvious questions that are often the best, as well as handling sensitive areas with tact and persistence.

Finally, the consultant needs to be good at communicating in a number of modes: producing simple diagrams that encapsulate a concept; verbal skills; writing; and, perhaps above all, working with graphs and spreadsheets. It helps to have the presentation skills to lead large and sometimes reluctant groups through understanding options to making decisions. Architects generally feel most at home with diagrams and least comfortable with numbers; unfortunately, the reverse is generally true for clients.

1 These qualities also appear in a longer list given by P. Barrett and C. Stanley, in *Better Construction Briefing*, Blackwell Science, 1999.
2 Procurement Guidance No 1: *Essential Requirements for Construction procurement*, H M Treasury. www.hmtreasury.gov.uk.gccp
3 See A. Ashworth, *Cost Studies of Buildings*, Addison Wesley Longman, Harlow, 1999.
4 Proving a quantifiable link between design and productivity has long been a holy grail for academics studying buildings in use. J. Vischer comes very close in *Environmental Quality in Offices*, Van Nostrand Reinhold, New York, 1989.
5 W. Bordass and A. Leaman, 'Environmental quality, the new agenda', BIFM Annual Conference, Cambridge, September 1998. Available at www.usablebuildings.co.uk
6 For further reading on the role of the facilities manager, especially in relation to offices, see W. McGregor and D. Then, *Facilities Management and Business Space*, Arnold, London, 1999.
7 For fuller discussion of this point see K. Allinson, *Getting There by Design*, Architectural Press, 1997.

5 Briefing for sustainable development

This chapter is a short introduction to sustainable development as it affects briefing. It sets the context for the detailed considerations that appear in the checklists in Chapters 9–12.

5.1 A paradox

The Architects Code states that:

Whilst Architects' primary responsibility is to their clients, they should nevertheless have due regard to their wider responsibility to conserve and enhance the quality of the environment and its natural resources.[1]

This statement neatly summarises the paradox that lies at the root of the notion of sustainable development. The prevailing culture sees land and nature as resources to be exploited for gain, but the environmental degradation caused by development has clearly brought us up against the limits of exploitation. Clients build primarily for economic gain, generally working within the accepted norms of economic life, including the exploitation of resources such as land, forests, energy and water. Even the smallest conventional construction project uses resources and generates pollution, so how can architects serve their clients while at the same time 'conserving and enhancing the quality of the environment'?

5.2 Why conventional development is no longer sustainable

To set the context, this section gives a brief overview of the primary global environmental problems that result from conventional economic activity.

A series of intergovernmental conferences over the last 25 years have recognised the severe nature of the threats that unrestrained development poses to the environment. Britain has made commitments to the Framework Convention on Climate Change, the Convention on Biological Diversity, and Agenda 21, which promotes action at the local level. The primary areas of concern are:

- increased levels of carbon dioxide (CO_2) emissions, which international scientists now agree are the most likely cause of climate change[2] (the burning of fossil fuels in vehicles, in industry and in buildings is the major impact, in which the construction industry plays a significant part)
- ozone depletion caused by the release of chlorofluorocarbons (CFCs) into the

atmosphere, which are still to be found in certain construction materials and cooling systems

- the extinction of species of wildlife linked to the destruction of habitat, which has occurred both worldwide and progressively in Britain as development has been allowed on Sites of Special Scientific Interest (SSSIs)
- air pollution caused by emissions from fossil fuels, the pollution of natural water sources by industrial wastes, the destruction of forests by acid rain, and the contamination of the oceans – all of which are associated with development as a whole and with the building industry in particular

These problems are exacerbated by unequal distribution of resources around the world (known as the *problem of equity*), and booming populations in poorer countries. There is also an awareness that the rate at which we exhaust non-renewable resources is at the expense of what will or will not be available to provide future generations with levels of material comfort similar to our own. This is known as the *problem of futurity*.

Fossil fuels are the most notable of these non-renewable resources. Buildings consume over half of the gas and oil produced globally, and are responsible for over half of the resulting emissions. Current projections suggest that there is about a 45-year supply of conventional oil and 65 years of gas left worldwide.[3] The key factor in reducing the environmental impact of most buildings is reduced energy consumption, and this usually reduces operating costs for a small additional initial investment.

These problems may be global, but they are the effects of many local actions, and every construction project offers an opportunity to address them, at least in so far as the clients have developed an understanding of the situation.

5.3 Meeting the needs

Briefing is about defining requirements, in order to inform building designs that meet clients' needs. Producing buildings that *do* meet needs rather than buildings that don't will considerably reduce waste of energy, materials, space and human effort. There is considerable room for improvement in this area alone, which will help to mitigate the environmental impacts of construction.

Needs can be defined in a number of ways, depending on the focus of attention. A well-known definition[4] proposes a hierarchy, with basic physiological needs such as air, water, food and shelter at the base, rising through needs for safety and security, to social, psychological and moral needs such as aesthetics, meaningfulness, self esteem and, ultimately, love and truth. While this is a helpful model, it is limited to individual needs. Other writers have taken a wider view, considering human needs in the context of the local community and of society in general; some have strayed into political approaches in their definitions. As awareness of environmental issues has increased, efforts have been made to define needs in ways that consider environmental factors, alongside individual, group and societal needs. Of these, no single simple scheme has been found sufficiently practical to recommend as a guideline for briefing, but the checklists in Chapters 9–12 list the relevant issues.

5.4 What can the briefing consultant do?

The consultant can start by always asking the question behind the apparent issue. Each requirement in the brief refers back to an activity (what people *do*) that the requirement supports. The activity in turn refers back to an objective in the role section, concerned with the users' organisational aims. This in turn derives from a policy of the client organisation. Policy is a matter of choice and decision, based on information. The briefing consultant can provide the information to inform environmental policy, which in turn will be reflected in the brief. Briefing is very much about educating clients and explaining the options, and of course not only in issues of environmental sustainability. Environmental considerations do not generally appear as requirements in the brief unless the clients have developed a reasoned environmental policy.

Ultimately there are two basic options, with shades of variation between them. Many decisions in briefing and design flow from the initial choice between the two:

- The first option proposes minor technical changes to present practice, and looks to future research to find solutions to longer-term problems, without accepting the need for any fundamental change in the underlying nature of development. It does not apply the precautionary principle to environmental issues, nor does it suggest any redesign of operational activities.
- The second option is radical. It reads the warning signs seen in, say, pollution and climate change as a direct result of the traditional economy and its exploitation of natural resources. It proposes a new appreciation of nature and human life that will change the way buildings and development are conceived.

Given the strength of the evidence, the first option is a minimal response; and carrying on as usual is completely untenable as a third option.

Architects ultimately build what their clients want and are prepared to pay for. There are facts, and there are many shades of opinion as to how to interpret the facts. There is almost unlimited scope for the education both of architects themselves and of their clients.

It is important that the briefing consultant understands where the clients stand in relation to the two options outlined above. Without an understanding of sustainability objectives, design guidelines and benchmarks are ineffectual. Simply adding on a few environmentally friendly objectives will do little to mitigate the effects of an inherently unsustainable project. Thinking about sustainability is fundamental to any project, and it starts with the role and objectives of the client organisation, probably in the period before formal briefing commences. If the clients wish to make all of their activities fundamentally environmentally sustainable, then the buildings they commission will reflect their core policies.

The first questions to ask committed clients, or clients open to the discussion, would be:

- Is the proposed new space really necessary?
- Could the operations that it will accommodate be accommodated in existing space?
- Could the operations be redesigned so as to be reduced in scale or avoided altogether?

These questions stem from the *clean technology* approach already in practice in industry.[5] This aims to prevent environmental pollution at source rather than mitigate its effects later. It is defined as:

A means of providing human benefit that overall uses fewer resources and causes less environmental damage than alternative means with which it is economically competitive.

The focus is on the human benefit rather than on products. For example, a clean technology solution to the problem of vehicle emissions would more likely be home working or places of employment located at public transport nodes than a more effective vehicle exhaust filter.

Finally, the clinching argument: sustainable solutions are invariably less expensive to operate and usually cost the same or little more than conventional buildings in initial capital outlay.

1   *The Architects Code, Standards of Conduct and Practice*, Architects Registration Board, December 1999.
2   Intergovernmental Panel on Climate Change, *Third Assessment Report*, Summary for Policymakers, Geneva, 2001. See www.ipcc.ch
3   U. Bartsch and B. Müller, *Fossil Fuels in a Changing Climate*, Oxford University Press, 2000.
4   Maslow's hierarchy of needs, quoted in a doctoral thesis: *Architectural Implications of Sustainability on Built Form*, by Peter Diprose, University of Auckland, 1998. This document is of extraordinary quality, and has informed arguments on sustainability throughout the present volume.
5   Rita van der Vorst, *The Development of Terminology for Environmental Protection*, Centre for Environmental Technology, Imperial College, London, 1999.

For further reading see:

S. Halliday, *Green Guide to the Architect's Job Book*, RIBA Publications, 2000.
Thermie Programme of the European Commision DGXVII, *A Green Vitruvius*
Sustainable Architectural Design, James & James Science Publishing 1999.
A number of excellent publications on improving energy consumption and sustainability in a wide range of building types produced by the Building Research Establishment, www.bre.org.
Publications on the use of renewable energy sources produced by Energy Technology Support Unit, www.etsu.com.
A number of excellent research articles on buildings, users and sustainability by W. Bordass and A. Leaman are available at www.usablebuildings.co.uk

6 Working with clients and users

This chapter is the first of three in which practical techniques are described. Together they constitute a briefing consultant's toolbox from which to select techniques suitable for most projects. The present chapter looks at some techniques for working with clients and user groups:

- interviews
- meetings
- defining quality
- creative problem-solving
- decision-making
- surveys
- building evaluation and site assessment
- opinion surveys

6.1 Interviews

Interviews are usually a part of the initial information-gathering stage. They are useful:

- in the initial stages of a project, when the need is to understand the key issues as seen by prominent members of the organisation
- to gather the views of key personnel with particular knowledge or influence who are not members of the working group

6.1.1 Initiating interviews

Interviews are arranged either by the consultant or by the clients' project coordinator. In either case, they are scheduled to make the best use of the consultant's time.

The interviewee will have been informed in advance of the date, time, length of interview and subjects to be covered and their context in the briefing project.

The interviewer will have an agenda listing questions, subject areas, objectives for the interview, or decisions to be made.

Should the interview notes be written up and circulated? This takes time, but gives interviewees an opportunity to correct misunderstandings. It is often adequate to substitute a check of the draft brief.

If resources allow, an assistant from the consultant's office can take notes, leaving the interviewer free to concentrate on the interview. Another possibility is to record interviews on tape, provided the interviewee has agreed to this; some people find a tape recorder threatening. It is possible to take notes and listen at the same time, but it is not easy to give the interviewee full attention while writing.

6.1.2 During the interview

During the interview, the consultant needs to:

- Treat everything he or she is told with respect, but listen especially to discern the few key issues — those that are critical for the success of the project — from the large quantity of information that will probably be provided. The interviewee will probably not be able to distinguish what is relevant from a number of issues that concern them but which may not be relevant to the brief.
- Categorise information from the start, distinguishing between role, activities and requirements — the main headings of the questionnaire. It is also important to distinguish between policy issues, relating to the strategy and direction of the organisation; management issues, relating to the organisation and direction of work; and operational issues, relating to the details of how activities are performed.
- Remind interviewees, if necessary, that new space can ease some operational problems, but cannot possibly solve policy or management issues. If these arise, they can be noted and reported back to the clients.
- Not promise what cannot be delivered. By asking questions, there is always a danger of raising expectations and appearing to offer the prospect of vastly improved accommodation. It is important to discover what people need and what they would choose in an ideal situation, but questions must always be prefaced by saying that nothing can be promised; that there are many factors to be considered, and that cost will be an issue. All that can really be promised is that the interviewee's contribution will be seriously considered.
- Keep an eye on the broader picture. The interviewee may hold an eccentric view or an extreme position. This may be far sighted — leading to great improvements — or merely peculiar. People change jobs quite frequently; will future holders of the position have similar requirements? The consultant needs to be sufficiently aware of best practice within the industry sector to spot eccentricities.

6.1.3 Interviews in general

After introductions and a limited amount of social conversation so that both parties feel comfortable with one another, the interviewer can check the following:

- the correct spelling of the interviewee's name and position
- that both are seated comfortably and equitably
- that the purpose of the interview is understood, its context in the briefing process and in the project as a whole

Questions are put from a prepared checklist or questionnaire, starting with general, open questions and moving into more specific questions and greater detail.

Listening is an art. The interviewer will understand how easy it is to hear what one is predisposed to hear rather than what is actually said. It is very difficult to listen and record clearly without bringing in personal bias.

Questions should be designed to expand on the answers that have been given. They should open up the discussion to clarify and find out more about significant areas. An initial statement is not necessarily the interviewee's final word on a subject.

Questions that produce a yes or no answer should be avoided, as should putting words in the interviewee's mouth or otherwise closing down the conversation. People are often encouraged to speak when the interviewer is silent, leaving the space to the interviewee.

At frequent intervals it is helpful to summarise what has been said, checking the interviewer's understanding of the interviewee's answers before moving on.

An awareness of non-verbal clues such as body language, posture and hesitations is useful. It is possible to listen not only for the meaning, but also for the emotion behind the words and the possible reasons for that.

Is the interviewer's own body language confident, relaxed, non-aggressive, attentive, interested and receptive? Empathy with the interviewee is maintained, listening rather than bringing oneself into the conversation. The more receptive the interviewer, the more the interviewee will feel able to confide and the more will be learnt.

As the interview progresses, there is a shift from general questions to the more detailed and specific.

6.1.4 Completing an interview

The interview should end on time. It is concluded by summarising what has been understood or agreed. This is particularly important if the informant is not to have a chance to check written interview notes later.

The interviewee will need to know what happens next. Where more work is required, the consultant proposes an action plan, agreeing specifically who will do what, and by what dates.

Issues for the interviewee to take away for further consideration or to discuss with colleagues are identified. The date, time and place of any further meetings are confirmed and the participant thanked for their help and their time.

Notes should be transcribed as soon as possible, while the memory is still fresh.

6.2 Meetings

Taking possession of the meeting room 10 minutes before the meeting starts gives the briefing consultant time to check environmental conditions and controls, that audio-visual equipment works, and that there is a spare projector bulb.

Once the briefing process starts, the briefing consultant should take the chair at meetings of the steering committee and working groups.

The first meeting starts with introductions. Each participant can be invited to make a short statement about their role, responsibilities and expertise, and their objectives, role and responsibilities in the project.

In chairing the meeting, the consultant needs to:

- have a clear series of objectives for the meeting to achieve
- introduce the agenda at the start of the meeting and use it to guide the discussion
- if necessary, make it clear (tactfully) that junior members have much to contribute, and should be encouraged to do so
- use the position of the chair firmly, to stop long-winded, high-handed or otherwise unhelpful contributions, should they crop up
- offer a comfort break after about 45 minutes and certainly after an hour

The aim is to establish informed consensus.

Establishing consensus in the client briefing team involves building a team that is enthusiastic, and focused on moving the project forward. Procedures should be established for communicating between team members between meetings, and for communication with the consultant. Members should agree to communicate with their constituencies within the organisation and on how the organisation as a whole will be kept informed.

6.2.1 Subsequent meetings

The consultant starts and finishes subsequent meetings by reviewing progress and the agenda. It is even better if the agenda is circulated in advance. The meeting is guided through new material with individual copies, an overhead or computer presentation. It can be assumed that participants will not have read new material prior to a meeting, so it need not be circulated in advance.

The consultant-facilitator should pause at intervals to summarise what has been said, confirm decisions made, confirm progress against the agenda, and define the next task. The facilitator's role is to lead the meeting through a series of decisions, explaining the options and implications of each. It is to be encouraging, giving recognition for achieving agreement on a difficult issue.

It is important to be considerate of the perceived threat that change poses to staff and other building users. Information, consultation and reasoned argument diffuse fears and imaginings. Not everyone may welcome change, but they will generally accept it, if the objectives and reasoning are understood. Acceptance increases if users feel they have been honestly consulted and listened to in the decision-making process.

6.2.2 Ending the meeting

At the end of the meeting, the consultant summarises what has been achieved and thanks the participants. Any tasks to be undertaken by members of the group before the next meeting are agreed. The time and place for the next couple of meetings are confirmed and the tasks to be achieved outlined.

It is important to end on time, and to be very respectful of people's time. If more time is needed, an additional meeting can be arranged. More can be achieved in a number of focused one-hour meetings than in fewer meetings that drift on for half a day.

6.3 Defining quality

It is generally not too difficult to define requirements where objectives can be framed as measurable values or benchmarks. When discussing qualities, rather than quantities, one sometimes struggles for language that both the client group and the design team will understand. Vague adjectives such as 'good quality' or 'high standard' may be meaningful to the person using them, but they are open to misinterpretation. This is a particular problem when describing the clients' intentions for design quality, atmosphere and image. Adjectives sometimes work, especially if they are unusual or poetic, and are used to evoke atmosphere in a creative way. For example, the intended ambience of a new restaurant could be characterised as 'fresh, crisp, elegant, supportive, warming, translucent'. Better might be a collection of images that indirectly evoke the required qualities, or which show examples of analogous environments.

The danger of using these approaches, which come from the world of commercial brand design, is that the result can be ephemeral and superficial. However, with care, it is possible to use the technique with integrity and substantial content to capture a vision for the clients and communicate that to the design architect. This is of course not the same as compiling a library of building images to be imitated. It is good to distinguish between describing the quality of space that is sought and design approaches and styles, which should be largely be left to the design architect.

It is always essential to check that high aspirations are matched by available funds. Cars provide a useful analogy in the early stages of the project for understanding the clients' intentions, both for quality and for related cost.[1] The car is such a potent and pervasive cultural symbol that everyone understands the implications when the proposed new space is compared to, say, a Jaguar, a BMW, or a Mondeo.

An alternative approach that can be used to rate either experience of an existing environment or objectives for a new one is the *semantic differential scale*.[2] This consists of a list containing pairs of polar opposites, such as:

simple	___	___	___	___	___	___	___	complex
delicate	___	___	___	___	___	___	___	rugged
interesting	___	___	___	___	___	___	___	boring
broken	___	___	___	___	___	___	___	continuous
welcoming	___	___	___	___	___	___	___	forbidding
tight	___	___	___	___	___	___	___	loose
bold	___	___	___	___	___	___	___	timid
dreadful	___	___	___	___	___	___	___	delightful
cheerful	___	___	___	___	___	___	___	gloomy

Participants are asked to rate the option under discussion on a scale of 1 to 7 between each pair of carefully selected adjectives. The results can be simply collated or, for a larger sample, analysed statistically to show significant correlations between ratings.

6.4 Creative problem-solving

Techniques of creative problem-solving are based on the scientific understanding that the two sides of the brain function in different ways.[3] The left side of the brain tends to order, organisation, analysis, discipline, linear logic. It lacks an imaginative faculty, and keeps to known paths and conservative solutions. The right side of the brain is wildly imaginative, creative, intuitive, and inventive, but undisciplined. It produces original expressive art, novel designs, and original solutions. Both sides should ideally work in a complementary way: the right to generate fresh ideas, the left to sort, evaluate, select, and develop. Childhood education and conditioning in Western societies tends to produce people who favour the left, ordering side at the expense of the right, creative side. There are many techniques available that attempt to restore the balance by temporarily suspending or bypassing the left brain function.

These techniques work best in a relaxed, informal atmosphere, where people will not feel shy of offering thoughts that at first sight are ridiculous. Humour – and a playfulness – help. Architects feel quite at home in this sort of environment, and it is easy to underestimate how difficult it can be for people used to less creative cultures to relax sufficiently to participate.

6.4.1 Brainstorming

Brainstorming is a specific technique for producing fresh creative ideas for possible solutions. The term tends to be used to describe any unstructured discussion, but there is more to it than that. It is particularly useful in briefing when an issue has been identified and a briefing solution is required. It also works well for stimulating design approaches.

- The consultant acts as leader and chairs the process.
- A problem is defined in the form of a question.
- A time limit is set: say 6 minutes.
- The participants are asked to come up with as many ideas as possible, without discussion, without evaluation and without self-censorship. The wilder and more unexpected these are, the better.
- Participants are encouraged to build on each others' ideas or to suggest variations.
- The consultant notes down the ideas as they come on a flipchart, and stops the process when enough ideas have been gathered or the time limit has been reached.
- After the brainstorm is over, the group evaluates the ideas and picks the most promising three or four for further development and evaluation. Some evaluation methods are discussed below.

6.4.2 Nominal group technique

- The consultant defines the problem to be solved and sets a time limit, say 5 minutes.
- Members of the group, working individually, write down as many ideas or concerns as they can think of within the time.
- Each in turn reads out what they have written, allowing the group as a whole to sense the breadth of possibilities.
- It is quite all right to have nothing to say.
- The consultant notes ideas on a flipchart.
- The group selects the half dozen most promising ideas.
- These are ranked by the group in order of most promising, and are then evaluated.

6.4.3 Other solution-generating techniques

There are various other techniques for generating fresh ideas. Amongst them are *synectics*, in which the issue is compared with analogies from other disciplines, and in particular the natural sciences, in order to spark a solution to the current problem. In *free association* the problem is first stated, and then the consultant picks five words at random. Participants write down the first words that come to mind, triggered by random associations with the five: whatever leaps to mind. The group next looks for possible solutions brought to mind by analogy with the words they have written down. The ideas generated are ranked and evaluated.

6.5 Decision-making

Some client groups have little problem in reaching decisions; others are indecisive or fractious. Briefing meetings can become a battleground for long-held animosities and departmental rivalries. At other meetings, staff representatives wait to hear the view of a dominant management figure before venturing their own agreement. The atmosphere within an organisation is set by management, and to some extent the consultant has to work with the prevailing situation. The consultant can often use his or her special status as an outside expert to establish a problem-solving atmosphere within the meeting that will allow creative and rationally justifiable decision-making.

6.5.1 A problem-solving atmosphere

Whatever the culture of the client organisation, the consultant can establish a proper atmosphere for decision-making by example, and by intervention from the chair. Such an environment will have the following characteristics:[4]

- Every contribution is respected.
- Comments focus on the problem or issue, not on the person.
- There is empathy and consideration for the feelings that lie behind a position, without necessarily agreeing or disagreeing with it.
- The aim is to find solutions that are beneficial for all parties.
- Objective criteria are used to evaluate proposals and support selected options.
- Force of character, emotion and hierarchical status give way to rational discussion of possible solutions.
- A good solution will as far as possible meet the needs of everyone, including neighbours and other affected outsiders.
- Difficult issues are not avoided, but are handled rationally and with empathy for the concerns of participants.

There are certain phrases that are likely to crush innovation, and the consultant needs to listen for them and possibly warn against them. Some examples are:

- We've tried it before and it didn't work; why should it work now?
- It may work there but it won't work here.
- Let's set up a committee, or call in a consultant, to study it.
- It will be too expensive/cheap/radical/old fashioned/subtle/obvious/big/small/time-consuming etc.
- The boss (unions, minister, or other authority figure) will never accept it.
- It's against policy.
- Any sort of ridicule, faint praise, silence, or sarcastic comment.

The consultant also needs to be aware of senior members wishing to cut discussion short by making 'executive decisions'. Arbitrary decisions tend not to stick unless they are backed by reasoned argument and consensual agreement, and when they eventually do come unstuck the damage to the project is often extensive, creating considerable additional work for the consultant. The opposite tendency is no more helpful; there are people who tend to follow the herd in their opinions, and are likely to follow meekly when the majority view swings in one direction. It is worth drawing these people out and probing for their concerns and views, which may be valuable and otherwise overlooked.

6.5.2 Method and time

Decision-making takes time, but the consultant's time is often limited by commercial considerations – fees have been cut to a minimum in order to secure the commission. In terms of time, there are basically three approaches:

- The consultant is seen as an expert on building types, who will carry out a short survey and make recommendations with little or no consultation of people within the organisation. This approach is outdated and not generally recommended, although there may be a very few specialised situations where it is appropriate. Not much time is required, but the consultant should command a healthy fee.
- The consultant carries out surveys and makes observations, but does not involve staff in discussion. Department heads are consulted, and senior management take decisions on the basis of the consultant's survey analysis and recommendations. This takes a moderate amount of consultant time, and little staff time. Staff present their opinions through questionnaires and focus groups. Communication is from staff to consultant without much in the way of feedback.
- Management, staff, and other users at all levels participate in the development of the brief through a structured series of meetings in which management contribute as equals. Approvals are usually referred to senior management. Representatives speak for staff and users. This draws on knowledge at all levels of the organisation, and gives staff and users a large measure of influence over decisions. It takes time, but good organisation of the process ensures that the time is used productively. As the culture of organisations changes, as old hierarchies fade and the views of in-house specialists gain more respect, this approach should be increasingly appreciated. In voluntary organisations, such as residents' groups, meetings open to all – rather than meetings of representatives – may be the only acceptable form.

In any group decision-making process people will tend to favour first one view before swinging to its opposite. It may take some time for opinion to settle.

Decisions should not be made on material that has not been circulated or discussed at a previous meeting. Decisions made in haste or without consultation either produce poor results or do not last.

6.5.3 Rating and ranking

This is a technique for clarifying the view of a meeting when the time for a decision arrives. After various options have been defined, each member is asked to attach a score between 1 and 5 to each option. A very good option scores 5; a very bad one scores 1. After time for consideration, these are collected on a flipchart, and totals are added for each option. Members who disagree with the consensus are asked for their reasons. The technique gives a measure of the feeling in a meeting, which in itself can be useful, but is a rather crude tool for making final decisions.

A more refined method for ranking project objectives is as follows:[5]

1 The participants identify their objectives.
2 The objectives are given scores according to perceived value by each participant, and the scores are totalled for each objective.
3 A cut-off is set below which objectives are excluded as having insufficient merit, according to score. This can be related to the relative costs of implementation.
4 Each objective is compared with each other using a matrix. In the boxes of the matrix, the preferred option in each pair comparison is noted together with a new score on a scale of 1 to 3.
5 Scores are totalled for each objective, giving a ranking of objectives and comparative levels of approval by the group.
6 Taking the total of all scores as 100%, individual objective scores are expressed as percentages.
7 The ranked and scored objectives are set against costs of implementation at various levels of completeness. It may be agreed to meet only part – say 50% or 80% – of the objectuve if this provides optimal value against cost.

6.5.4 Consensus decision-making

In this technique each member states their preference for a defined option from among several. They explain their choice. When everyone present has expressed their view, going round the table without interruption, they each have a second turn at explaining and a third, strictly in turn around the table, until there is complete agreement. The aim is to focus on the objective arguments without bringing in personal preference, and to be open to persuasion by the argument of others. Again, no one pulls rank or denigrates the view of others. Equally, no one should give up their argument merely to shorten the discussion.

6.5.5 Issue sheets

This is a way of recording issues to be resolved and decisions taken, rather than a tool for making them. For each issue the consultant fills out a single A4 sheet divided into four sections. The issue to be resolved is given a title and defined in the first section. When the issue is fully understood, the options and their implications are briefly described in the second section. There will be a cost implication, and implication for programme, and possibly an implication for quality or project scope. When agreement is reached, the decision is recorded in the third section, together with any reasons. The fourth section is for the clients' signature and date. A set of issue sheets may form an appendix to the briefing document.

6.6 Surveys

If the users of the new space already occupy an existing building, it is obviously worth looking at how they use the space. There are three approaches to this sort of survey, each providing additional information and a finer level of detail:

- space audit
- occupancy survey
- activity survey

The appropriate level of detail will be taken according to the nature of the project.

6.6.1 Space audit

A space audit consists, at the simplest level, in mapping the space that the various functions or departments occupy. Taking measured occupied areas with staff numbers for each department provides a guide to area per person, which is an essential measure in certain building types. It enables the consultant to accurately compare the proposals in the brief with the existing situation, but it gives little information as to what is actually done within the space.

6.6.2 Occupancy survey

An occupancy survey adds to the information provided by the space audit survey by asking how effectively space is used. Is a space suited to its current use? For how much of the time is it used? Is it the right size for its use? Are the environmental quality and servicing appropriate to the needs?[6]

Examples
- A university may have various lecture theatres seating 60, but changes in course design have created a need for lecture theatres for 300, and have rendered the smaller theatres unusable.
- Records in a solicitors' office show that all the meeting rooms are in use throughout the day. An occupancy study reveals that they are indeed in constant use, but predominantly for meetings of four to six people rather than their capacity of 12.

The same approach can also be used for post-occupancy evaluation, to assess how well new space is working in practice following the completion of a project. In large organisations the lessons learnt from previous projects provide valuable information for the new brief.

6.6.3 Planning an occupancy survey

The first step is to clarify why the survey is needed, and what information it is intended to produce. Keeping the objectives few, simple and to the point increases the likelihood of success. Typical survey objectives in an office building might be to quantify:

- the occupancy of enclosed offices and open-plan workstations, by department and by staff category
- the use of meeting rooms and conference facilities
- the use of support facilities such as central copying

Once the survey objectives have been defined, the most cost-effective way of achieving them needs to be considered. It need not necessarily all be done by walking the floors with clipboards. Central copying will have records of copy order sheets. Meeting rooms do probably require regular survey visits, because they may be booked but not used, or may be used by a group much smaller than their capacity. Records should be checked of people entering and leaving the building, and of the use of desk phones and computers.

When planning the occupancy survey, decisions are needed on:

- what resource can be used for the survey
- who will carry it out
- what information is needed to make it possible, such as plans of the building
- how many people need to be surveyed
- whether a small sample will produce accurate results
- how many days the survey should cover
- how frequently observations should be made
- what locations should be surveyed
- whether both moving and static people will be counted
- whether data will be collected manually or on computers
- how the data will be analysed
- how the findings will be interpreted
- when the results will be available
- whether the quality of the information produced will justify the disruption and cost

6.6.4 Observation during an occupancy survey

In general, observation over several working days in a single week provides robust results, provided the week is typical. This means avoiding surveying during school holiday periods, snowstorms or rail strikes. The locations to be surveyed must be defined clearly: a location may be a room, but the boundaries of a workstation in open-plan space require clear definition. A route between survey locations needs to be mapped out, and each location visited at hourly intervals during the day. The length of day needs discussion: is it 9.00 to 5.00, or does it make sense to start at 8.00 or earlier, and continue until 6.30 or later? Where there is an extended working day, as in a hospital, university library, or some offices, visits are extended to cover evenings, nights and weekend working. Access must be possible to all survey locations, and the people to be surveyed must be warned to expect interruptions, but without giving survey times; forewarning people of survey dates and times may influence their behaviour. A short explanation of the survey should be circulated to those involved; this will contain the name of the clients' project coordinator, who will handle any questions or problems.

The survey team needs to be clear about what is to be recorded and how. Will the record be kept with pencil and paper, or with a hand-held computer? Possible observations should be categorised:

- the number of people present
- activity – sitting, standing, talking, holding a meeting, operating a machine, phoning, operating a computer, etc.
- the identity of those present

Some clients will prefer to provide their own personnel to carry out the survey, under the consultant's supervision. This can work well, provided surveyors are free of other obligations during the survey. Their inside knowledge will be an asset.

6.6.5 Processing and interpretation

Manual survey sheets should be designed for easy entry of data into a computer. With a hand-held computer, the entry format should be easy to use, and the resulting data should be transferable to a larger computer for sorting, analysis and presentation. It also helps if data entry mistakes can be easily corrected,

Transferred into graph form, the survey data should show up patterns. For instance, activities for various categories of user may fall into patterns, such as mainly in, mainly out, or in and out. Specific jobs may have clear patterns: sales staff, government inspectors or accounts auditors may be mainly out. There may be times in the week or in the day when more staff are in or out. Specific hierarchical grades may have clear patterns: managers will probably spend more time in meetings than was thought, leaving expensive offices empty. Survey data should be checked for reliability against interview and focus group notes, or other available confirming evidence. The results are verified by comparison with other surveys of similar operations.

6.6.6 Activity survey

An activity survey adds to the utilisation survey an examination of the operations themselves. It focuses on describing what people do – to some extent independently of where they do it. Having described the daily activities that go on in a department or a whole organisation, there is an opportunity to take a fresh look at the design of operations, and to question whether it is arranged in the best way. Routines often persist long after the original circumstances have changed. New technology has been introduced but not integrated into working practices. Operations have been warped by the idiosyncrasies of old buildings. The survey simply records what activities are undertaken during the course of the working day, and asks why. The process of observation and description often raises issues for clients, and suggests simplification. Management in an organisation are often so close to day-to-day operations that they do not always see the pattern of what their staff actually do.

What distinguishes an activity survey from an occupancy survey is descriptions of intention. It looks not only at what is done but at why it is done: how one activity relates to another, and how they relate to objectives within the business plan. The consultant is looking not for mechanistic relationships between objective and activity, but for a clear purpose behind operations, and a clear flow of work geared to meeting objectives.

Examples
- A study of activities was carried at an airport to re-examine check-in and security procedures, and to establish what travellers, airline and terminal staff wanted and needed at each stage of the process between passengers' entering the airport and taking off.
- A study of procedures and the flow of work was carried out in a financial services office to define flows of work prior to interior fit-out of a new building.
- The daily routine of care and of staff procedures in an institution for medically dependent, multi-handicapped infants was observed and analysed as part of a briefing study for a major renovation.

The survey is carried out through observation, interviews, client group meetings and questionnaire surveys, depending on the circumstances. Still and video photography can be useful in recording activity changes throughout the working day, or to illustrate issues for later discussion.

6.7 Building evaluation and site assessment

6.7.1 Building evaluation

A building evaluation assesses the suitability of a building for a client organisation.[7] It looks at the constraints and opportunities afforded by space in a newly acquired building or within an existing building, against the clients' defined requirements. A building may be very good in itself but not suit the defined needs of the client organisation. Options for leasing new space can be evaluated and compared against criteria such as location, accessibility, floor area, number of floors, plan form, column spacing, or type and capacity of engineering services. It is often necessary to evaluate options for new space before the brief is fully developed. A draft brief will often be sufficient or, alternatively, a short assessment of client requirements against standards typical of the building type.

It may be that a building survey is required in addition, assessing general construction and condition, or specialist investigations into such areas as mechanical or electrical services, structure, or fire prevention and means of escape.

6.7.2 Site assessment

Though not strictly part of briefing in the sense of 'defining the problem to which the building will be a solution', a site assessment is often required alongside briefing in order to test the feasibility of the brief. As with a building evaluation, the question is not whether the site is good, but whether it meets the client organisation's particular requirements. Each site will have unique characteristics, constraints and opportunities, and a potential floor area capacity. In the end the choice of site may be swayed by investment decisions, or by the particular strength of a single characteristic such as location. Site assessment is a separate exercise from a site survey, which seeks to establish boundaries, topology, access routes, microclimate, planning constraints, covenants and other legal restrictions, and exactly what there is above and below ground: drains, old foundations, trees and planting, water courses, utilities, site pollution, etc. A site survey may be required to inform the site assessment.

6.8 Opinion surveys

In large organisations, the time and resources may not be available to work with representative groups at a departmental level. There are also groups with little formal organisation, and with variable commitment to cooperation in briefing; they may be transient, such as public transport passengers, or have minimal organisation, such as local residents. Surveys can be used both to collect opinion on key issues and to gauge preferences for options. Surveys are not creative in the way that meetings and workshops can be; they are unlikely to produce new solutions. They might be used:

- where the client is a very large organisation, and the creation of a structure of representative groups is too time consuming or otherwise unacceptable to management
- where the client is a developer, and the building user is not known, so that an opinion survey in organisations similar to the proposed tenant will provide up-to-date information on requirements
- for comparing the clients' briefing proposals with practice elsewhere in their industry sector
- in finding out what large volumes of customers, passengers, patients, guests, students or other consumers of services think of buildings they use and of future proposals
- in gauging the reaction of the general public in the neighbourhood or more generally to proposals

Before designing a survey instrument, the consultant must be clear as to the objectives of the survey. This entails:

- designing the survey instrument so that analysis of the results is simple, and can be computerised
- understanding enough about the area to know the issues involved
- designing questions to give simple, precise answers such as yes, no, or a number
- avoiding bias in the way the questions are framed
- in small surveys, being very clear who is to be asked and why, and being sure that they are representative
- where opinions are sought, asking for a rating on a scale of 1 to 5
- including no more than one open-ended opinion question – these can produce valuable insights, but are difficult to analyse

It is always best to use a specialist consultant for larger surveys. The design of a survey instrument is a skilled undertaking, in which precise wording is crucial. In all but the simplest surveys there is a danger of statistical error distorting the results.[8]

1 See W. Peña with W. Caudill and J. Focke, *Problem Seeking*, Cahners Books International, Boston, 1977. This is one of the fundamental texts of American briefing practice, and still relevant.
2 See R. Hershberger in M. Palmer ed. *The Architect's Guide to Facilities Programming*, The American Institute of Architects, Washington, 1981, p. 82.

3   For further reading on creative problem-solving, see R. McKim *Experiences in Visual Thinking*, Brooks/Cole, Monterey, Calif, 1980.

4   On the subject of communication in difficult situations, M. B. Rosenberg *Nonviolent Communication, A Language of Compassion*, 1999, www.cnvc.org, is highly recommended.

5   This technique is based on that used in value engineering procedures by Dr R. Woodhead of Oxford Brookes University. www.brookes.ac.uk/other/veamac

6   I am grateful to Joanna Eley and Alexi Marmot of AMA, London, for information on AMA's survey method, www.aleximarmot.com.

7   For further reading on building assessment see F. Becker, *The Total Workplace*, Van Nostrand Reinhold, New York, 1990, p. 261 ff. This discusses office buildings, but the principles are transferable to other building types.

8   There are a number of general books on social survey technique. J. Zeisel, *Inquiry by Design: Tools for environment-behaviour research* Cambridge University Press, 1984, deals specifically with survey technique in relation to the built environment.

7 Presentations and reports

This chapter discusses the organisation and design of presentations, reports and other work delivered to the clients as the products of the briefing exercise. In the first section it discusses some overall principles of presentation for briefing; it then looks at five techniques:

- flow diagrams
- relationship matrix
- relationship diagram
- spreadsheet charts
- visualising size

7.1 Presenting the brief

A brief is addressed to two readerships: the client group and the design team. They have rather different needs. Both need an overall summary but, in addition, the design team needs considerably more detail. There will of course be individuals in the client group, such as the clients' project coordinator, who will need to understand and approve the detail, but senior decision-makers want the bones of the story on a single side of paper. This is the executive summary that should preface every consultancy report, and it may well be all that a senior decision-maker will read. On the other hand, everyone likes a well-structured computer slide presentation that delivers briefing information in a series of easily digested headline statements.

7.1.1 Organising an oral presentation

During the process of fact finding, research, surveys, interviews and meetings, a great deal of information will have been gathered. It is wise to organise this information according to the sections of the final brief: that is, information should be organised for easy access by its readers or audience. The presentation is, in effect, telling a story, and the order in which it is told is very similar for most projects. A typical order for a presentation is:

1 Contents
2 Cost
3 Purpose of the project
4 Background to the project, and major issues it will solve
5 Role of the user organisation
6 Key objectives within the role

7 Activities that will take place within the new space
    projected staffing
    flows of work
8 Requirements, including
    floor area requirements, component by component or space by space
    design guidelines
    proximities and relationships between spaces, if relevant
    benchmarks for detailed performance
9 Programme

This list has nine main headings; in a computer slide presentation, it should take roughly 12 to 15 main slides. Behind each of these, held in reserve, will be another three or four slides that give the detail. These are shown only in answer to questions. An audience will expect digested, organised information, featuring any major recommendations, and backed up with detail if required. No one wants to hear the chronological story of the briefing consultant's work on the project. It is usual to have paper copies of a slide presentation to distribute to the client group before they leave. For smaller projects, or where the technology is not available, oral presentations can be accompanied by overhead projector slides, by boards at A3 or larger, or by A4 paper hand-outs.

7.1.2 A written report

A written report will have a format similar to a presentation but with more detail.

Very fine, dense detail will be presented either as a separate report, as for instance in a brief for detailed design, or as an appendix. The design team needs the detail in a form that is easily accessible to them: first, design guidelines for the project as a whole and, at a later stage, a series of data sheets for each space, in which information appears in the same order on each sheet. Chapters 10 and 11 give checklists for briefs for building design and detailed design respectively. An outline format for a typical brief document is given in Chapter 12. Depending on the type of brief, the details of the format will vary, as for instance in a brief for a campus master-plan, or a development brief that includes a plan for establishing an organisation that had not previously existed.

7.1.3 Appendices

Information that might be put in appendices includes:

- detailed staff projections
- detailed schedule of existing space

- site survey
- occupancy and activity survey details
- historical data
- detailed cost breakdown
- cost–benefit studies

Numerical data from appendices can be summarised as diagrams in the main document or presentation. Sophisticated illustrations can be produced using spreadsheet software, while the spreadsheets themselves remain in the appendix.

7.2 Flow diagrams

A flow diagram shows the movement of people, work, materials or traffic through a process that the new space will accommodate. It is the result of an activity analysis, as described in Chapter 6. Flow diagrams are crucial in some buildings and of little relevance in others; they have little application in most office buildings.

A flow diagram focuses on a sequence of activities rather than the spaces in which they occur. It frees up thinking about process before fixing activities in particular spaces. For example, Figure 7.1 shows the processing of specimens through a palaeontological museum. This is not a complete diagram for the building; there are separate flows of visitors through the museum, of other materials, and of staff. This sort of analysis helps to establish the necessary relationships between spaces and components: that is, groups of spaces.

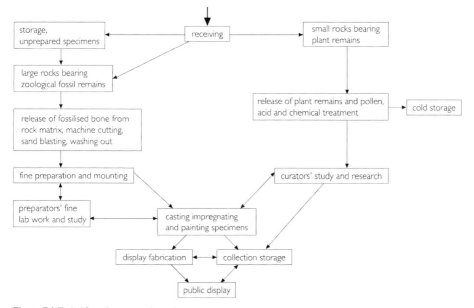

Figure 7.1 Typical flow diagram: specimens in a museum

7.3 Relationship matrix

This analysis suits some building types more than others; again, it is not usually crucial in office buildings. The information for the matrix is gathered during interviews and client meetings. It is primarily designed to show degrees of proximity between spaces, but it can be a useful way to show other information as well. It is a preliminary step in producing a *relationship diagram*, also known as a *bubble diagram*.[1]

7.3.1 Creating a relationship matrix

The steps in creating the matrix are as follows:

1 Using interview and meeting notes, make a numbered list of required relationships. Flow diagrams may be an additional source.
2 Develop a list of required spaces.
3 Number each required relationship sequentially.
4 Create the matrix grid, relating every space to every other.
5 Fill out the matrix in rough, entering a number referring to each relationship in the list.
6 Discuss this draft with the client group, refine and re-present the matrix.

The matrix will show several degrees of proximity, using numbers or symbols:

- continuous – two or more functional areas within a single physical space, with or without some definition of boundaries
- interconnecting – a door or opening connecting two spaces
- adjacent – next door along a circulation route
- very close
- close

An alternative method denotes the importance of realising the relationship rather than the degree of closeness. Using this approach, relationships may be marked as mandatory, strongly preferred, or simply desirable. It is not easy to use both methods in a single diagram.

Where there is no definite relationship, the square is left blank. When offered the option, a client group will tend to ask for many relationships. It is then necessary to sift out the key relationship, aware that, from the viewpoint of design, fewer are more likely to work, both functionally and aesthetically.

The matrix in Figure 7.2 is at a preliminary feasibility stage; it is part of a document that establishes the scope of a new organisation and its building. It does not show

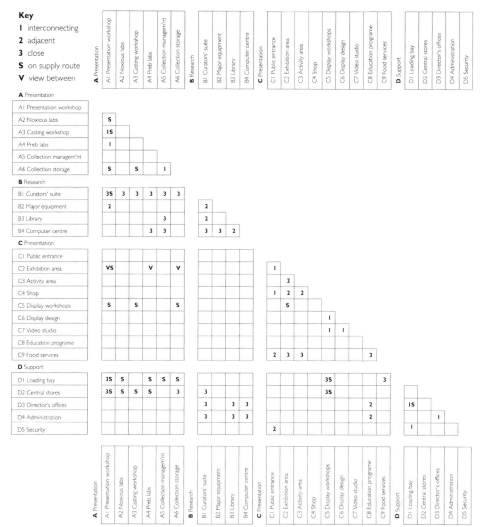

Figure 7.2 Relationship matrix for a museum

individual spaces, but elements – that is, small groups of closely related spaces – arranged to form components that coincide with operational functions. A more detailed matrix showing individual spaces will be constructed at a later stage.

7.3.2 Interpreting a relationship matrix

Looking at the matrix in Figure 7.2 one can make some interpretations:

- In addition to three numbered degrees of proximity, letters denote elements linked by a supply route and those where a view is required.
- The supply route for transporting large objects will be a major generator of

the design, linking preparation workshops, collection storage, loading bay, and central stores.
- There are no requirements for closeness between presentation and either preservation or research.
- Overall, not many boxes are filled, and, of those that are, the majority are for a 'close' relationship, the least demanding degree.
- There are clusters of interconnecting and adjacent relationships along the central diagonal, denoting relationships within rather than between components. These confirm the grouping of functions into meaningful components.
- The curators' suite is central to preservation and research components, requiring four 'close' but only two 'adjacent' relationships.
- There is also a 'close' relationship between the curators' suite, the director's office and administration.
- Requirements for views of the preservation work areas from public exhibition spaces may be difficult to satisfy.
- Looking at which spaces may require long spans, there are not many interconnecting or adjacent relationships between long- and short-span spaces.
- There are groups of long-span spaces with clusters of short-span support spaces, which will have implications for design.
- There is a clear progression of spaces in the non-public, backstage zone, but public access is limited to display spaces and their supporting areas.

The analysis may be taken further by identifying the comparative size of spaces, those that need access to the exterior, those that require potential for expansion, etc. It leads to the relationship, or bubble, diagram.

7.4 Relationship diagram

The relationship diagram is designed to show the relationships between spaces and their approximate relative sizes (see Figure 7.3). By using circles it avoids the connotations of building design. For simplicity, this diagram, like the last, shows elements and components, rather than individual spaces, which would be shown at a later stage in more detailed diagrams.

Two types of links are shown joining components: a solid line showing circulation of staff and visitors, and a dashed line showing staff circulation along a supply route, probably with an overhead crane gantry. More information about circulation could have been shown: for instance, different line styles to distinguish public from staff circulation, and varying line thickness to indicate the intensity of expected traffic. An overlay might show typical intended public flows and their volumes. The diagram could be overlaid with symbols denoting security barriers and checkpoints, or with tones to denote requirements for long-span, high spaces. All this is done without designing the building.

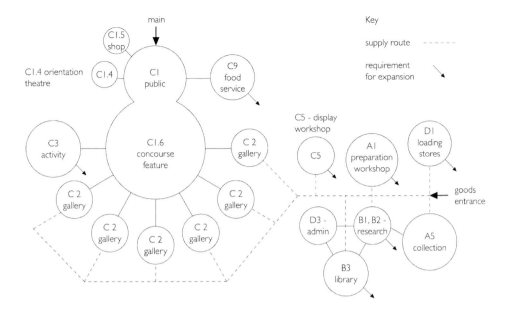

Figure 7.3 Relationship diagram for a museum

7.5 Spreadsheet charts

Figure 7.4 shows how a company is aiming to consolidate its use of space over several years from five buildings into two. Created using spreedsheet software, the chart shows the company's demand for space as a heavy black line. In years 1 and 2 demand decreases as a result of re-planning. Over the first three years the company vacates small amounts of space in three buildings, and plans to acquire new space in year 4 to prepare for occupancy in year 5. Demand remains stable as slack space is taken up in year 3, but the company hopes to expand, and will require additional space midway through year 6, depending on the rate of expansion.

Figure 7.5 is a very simple but effective chart, which shows the percentage distribution of total area between components in the museum example.

7.6 Visualising size

Clients often have problems with visualising the spatial implications of their requests. Perhaps they have described activities, furniture and equipment in a space; the consultant recommends a certain floor area to accommodate the function, and the clients cannot visualise what that would look like. The difficulty is in giving an accurate impression without creating a design. A number of approaches can be used:

Figure 7.4 Demand for space against space available

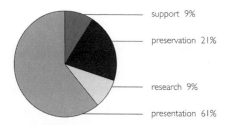

support 9%

preservation 21%

research 9%

presentation 61%

Figure 7.5 Space distribution

- often simplest is best: a simple scaled line drawing showing furniture and equipment
- comparing the floor area to rooms in the clients' existing space or other similar spaces in other buildings, actually or in photographs
- marking out floor areas with tape on the floor of the clients' space
- create three-dimensional CAD drawings with figures to show scale (these should be simple and almost diagrammatic)

In critical areas that are repeated a number of times in a large project, the consultant should consider building a full-size mock-up during the design stage. This is design by prototype, and is quite appropriate for spaces such as hotel rooms, hospital bed areas, or office workstations.

1 For an extraordinarily rich description of how to create and analyse a relationship matrix and use it in the development of a design, see E.T. White, *Space Adjacency Analysis*, Architectural Media Ltd, Tucson, 1986.

8 Areas and costs

Whatever else goes into a brief, a list of spaces and areas is an absolute minimum. The aim, initially, is to build a space budget, which can be looked at from several viewpoints:

- as the space that is required to meet functional requirements
- as the space that will fit into an existing building or onto a site
- as the space that can be provided within a fixed budget

Any or all of these conditions may apply in a project. As cost generally grows with floor area, the cost of functions within a building can roughly be controlled by controlling the area allocated to each. This is not quite the complete picture because other factors also influence cost, among which are:

- the quality of components and finishes and their intended life
- site-specific considerations such as existing buildings or special foundations
- requirements for functions with much higher than average cost
- the choice of procurement route
- construction market conditions at the time of tendering
- changes in the national economy in the period between briefing and construction

These and other exceptions aside, managing the space budget is a crude but effective way to manage the construction budget during briefing. In many buildings, only a third to a half of the space will be devoted to the core activity of the organisation; the remaining space will be 'spent' on circulation, plant, storerooms, catering facilities and other supporting functions.

8.1 Working with areas

8.1.1 Area categories

There are well-accepted methods of defining and measuring space. The terminology derives from the commercial office sector. Other building types have varying terminology based on similar principles. These measures are central to briefing, and are the vital statistics of any design. Briefing consultants and designers would do well to allocate space consciously, and understand the ratios between categories.

- *Gross external area (GEA).* This is the total building floor area on all floors measured to the outside of the external walls.

- *Gross internal area (GIA).* This is the total building floor area measured to the inside of the external walls.
- *Net internal area (NIA).* This is GIA less core areas. 'Core' includes such areas as stairs, lifts, lobbies, entrance lobby, toilets, plant areas and ducts. In leased space, core areas are a function of building design, and cannot usually be incorporated into operational space by tenants. In an air-conditioned building, the size of core areas in relation to GIA will be substantially higher than in naturally ventilated buildings.
- *Net lettable area (NLA).* This term is commonly used by property-letting agents in marketing material and lease documents. It is roughly equivalent to NIA, but its accuracy cannot be relied upon unless confirmed by an independent measured survey, and it should not be used in briefing.
- *Net usable area (NUA).* This is the area that can be occupied by user functions: it is NIA less primary circulation. 'Primary circulation' consists of major internal routes that give access to departmental spaces and functions and serve as means of escape. In open-plan buildings there may be some choice as to the layout of primary circulation. In these cases NUA is a function of detailed space planning rather than of the building shell. In other, probably older, buildings primary circulation is a fixed function of building design.

8.1.2 Area categories of buildings in use

The area definitions that follow are a function of how the building is used. There are many ways in which a modern building can be fitted out for use. In older, masonry buildings the choices may be fewer, and the use will be more closely determined by the building design itself.

- *Support areas.* This is space for functions that support the core activities of the organisation or building as a whole.
- *Usable operations area (UOA).* In office buildings, UOA is 'usable office area'. It consists of NUA less total support areas. It is the area available for office work. There are equivalents in most building types, though the terminology may be different.
- *Ancillary areas.* These are local support functions within departments or workgroups.
- *Secondary circulation.* This is circulation joining individual workstations to ancillary functions and primary circulation.
- *Workstation area.* This is UOA less ancillary and secondary circulation. In an office, this is the footprint of a workstation, with individual storage and a share of the secondary circulation that passes it.

Table 8.1 Examples of area categories in four building types

	Support area	Usable operations area	Ancillary areas	Workstation areas

Office	• reception
	• central filing
	• computer suite
	• conference room
		• open and cellular
		  office areas
			• local:
			  meeting rooms
			  photocopier
			  shared filing
				• desk
				  filing individual

School	• offices • dining hall • learning resources centre • caretaker's room	• classroom • gymnasium	• resource area • classroom store • student storage • equipment store	• student desk
Theatre	• box office • dressing rooms • scenery shops	• auditorium • lobby • stage	• prompt box • flies	
Restaurant	• kitchen • stores	• dining area • bar	• bus station	• cover (diner's place) • kitchen workstation

Table 8.1 shows how this scheme for defining area can be applied in four building types. Figure 8.1 shows an indicative proportional breakdown of areas in the four building types. Figure 8.2 shows the same approach extended to a detailed breakdown of space in offices. Note the comparatively small area that remains for workstations compared with the gross external area.

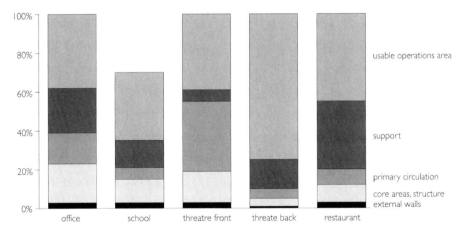

Figure 8.1 Indicative proportions of areas in four building types

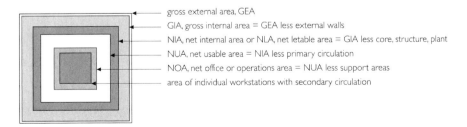

Figure 8.2 Detailed breakdown of areas in an office

Standard categories of space measurement such as these allow buildings to be compared. Percentage space allocations can be used in the brief as benchmarks to express facility objectives and later for evaluating design proposals. This approach is used, with varying terminology, in official design guidance for publicly funded buildings.

Every brief will contain a list of spaces, with their areas totalled as net usable area. This figure, by departments and for the whole building, is multiplied by suitable factors to arrive at gross internal and gross external areas.

One way of creating a sense of high quality is to provide more space than is required for strictly functional purposes. Atria in offices, lobbies in theatres and hotels, and generous circulation areas generally can all be used to create a sense of prestige and celebration. Designers will do this intuitively; these methods define requirements for such approaches so that they are foreseen and budgeted.

For large buildings the brief is compiled from the bottom up, listing individual and shared requirements, function by function, department by department, and adding in support functions. Percentages are added to net usable area to allow for primary circulation, structure, core, mechanical plant and external areas, arriving at a target gross external area. This space budget is controlled by checking against the total area affordable within the budget. When working with existing buildings the check is to ensure that required space fits the available building envelope. A fit factor will be applied to allow for the gap between the theoretical space budget and planning in the real building. In a modern office building this may be 2–3%; in an old building it may be as high as 20%. In some situations the departmental requirements are checked against agreed departmental space allocations. In this balancing process, initially, demand for space usually exceeds supply. The choice is between providing for all functions at reduced standards or omitting a complete function. Reduced space standards can sometimes be offset by increasing the quality of finishes and furniture.

8.2 Working with costs

Architects may see the construction contract cost as the sole measure of cost: that is, an initial one-off lump sum. It may be more helpful to look at construction as the first of a series of costs that the building will incur over its lifetime. In many buildings, initial cost will not even be the largest element of global lifetime costs.[1]

Clients are likely to ask about cost from the first day. It is both useful to the project and reassuring to the client if the briefing consultant can speak knowledgeably about cost when the subject comes up. First cost estimates tend to stick in the clients' minds, and any change will require lengthy explanations of the perceived increase. It may be better to express costs in the early stages as a range. As the brief is amended and refined, and as the design is developed, the cost will be similarly refined.

8.2.1 Costing the brief

Each statement in a brief carries a cost implication, and a brief that does not address both time *and* cost is somehow incomplete. Costs for small projects can be estimated with the help of a construction price book, tempered by some knowledge of local market conditions. On larger projects, the assistance of a quantity surveyor is usual, but there is nothing to prevent a competent briefing consultant from applying the same method and consulting the same sources as the specialist cost consultant, especially in the earlier stages of the project when broad budget figures are required. At least in the initial stages, one can use commercial price books giving costs per square metre for a list of building types.[2] These figures do not allow for the costs of special site conditions, any exceptional features, professional fees and VAT, or for the time elapsed between briefing and construction.

As a larger project progresses beyond the draft brief stage it is cost-effective to use a quantity surveyor, who will do the work faster and should be more aware of the market. Just as all architects are not equally at home with both briefing and design, so briefing requires a cost consultant who enjoys thinking strategically and modelling costs surrounded by uncertainties. Based on the final brief document, the quantity surveyor will create a preliminary cost plan, with figures for each element of the building: site works, drainage, foundations, floors, etc. These will be refined as the brief moves into design, but will still be provisional until an outline design has been produced. The cost estimate at the final brief stage should be accurate to within 5% either way of the tender price – not markedly less accurate than an estimate at tender stage.

8.2.2 Initial cost and cost in use

There is always the choice of specifying a more durable and usually more expensive solution, in the expectation of savings in the longer term through longer life expectancy and lower maintenance costs. It is necessary to understand early on in the process where the client stands in principle on this issue. Cost in use includes not only building maintenance and repairs, but also costs of insurance, taxes, cleaning, security, reception, computer and communication systems, landscape maintenance, car parking and the complete infrastructure that supports the organisation's core business. If issues of specification and design are not addressed at the briefing stage, there is much less opportunity to manage them later.

8.2.3 Life cycle and whole life costing

Life cycle costing recognises that elements of a building have varying life expectancies. Roofs may need major repair after 10–15 years and replacement after 20–30 years. Interior finishes in retail shops may be replaced after 2 years; air-conditioning systems have a life of 10–15 years. Good data exists on the life expectancy of building elements and of materials.[3] A building structure with a life of at least 60 years, and probably much more, will see several replacement cycles of its elements. The most frequent replacements are of some of the most expensive elements, such as mechanical services and fittings. In addition there are less predictable costs of internal alterations due to changes of use, extensions and the like for which allowance can be made. Of course, whenever there are major alterations the building must be brought up to the standards of the current building regulations, which, along with health, safety and access regulations, are continuously being strengthened. Assumptions can be made for the costs of alterations, repairs, replacements, redecoration, maintenance and cleaning over a defined lifespan for the building.

Whole life costing is life cycle costing extended to take into account costs over the whole life of a building from clay and metal in the ground and trees in the forest to rubble in a landfill site and material in an architectural salvage yard following demolition. It supersedes life cycle costing, which is defined fairly narrowly and deals only with the central part of a building's life, from construction and occupancy through to vacation. However cost is defined, the building user pays not only for the initial construction of the building but for borrowing costs, developer's profit, repairs, replacements, alterations, improvements, fuel costs, etc. as long as the user owns or occupies the building.

If the clients have adopted objectives for sustainability, one would also calculate the complete cost of depleting natural resources, the cost of transporting materials, of fuel used in manufacturing products, in heating and lighting the building, social costs, the cost of waste and emissions from the building, the cost of pollution in transporting people to and from the building, landfill costs, etc. At a time when the 'polluter pays' principle is not always fully applied, the question 'cost to whom?' is relevant, and the parameters or boundaries of the calculation require careful consideration.

However cost is defined, taking that cost over an agreed lifetime and adding the costs of land and initial construction gives a sum that can be converted to an annual cost of occupancy.[4]

8.2.4 Annualising costs

A useful way of expressing and comparing costs is to convert lump sums into the annual cost of repaying a mortgage taken out to cover the sum. On commercial projects, carried out with borrowed money, annualising or amortising costs is useful in comparing spending, borrowing and anticipated revenue from rents. Sophisticated clients will budget for costs over their expected occupancy of the building and make choices on qualities of materials and systems accordingly. As with any mortgage calculation, the term of the mortgage, principal sum borrowed and rate of interest that can be obtained all affect the annual cost of repayment.

8.2.5 Cost–benefit analysis

Cost–benefit analysis is a method for comparing options in order to select the one offering best value. It is an essential procedure at the option appraisal stage, but can also be applied throughout briefing whenever a choice needs to be made between two or more options. It uses money at today's value as a common denominator for comparing otherwise incomparable benefits. It has a role in a similar exercise, *investment appraisal*, in which the aim is to assess whether an adequate return can be made on an investment.

Money values are placed on the effects of each option. This is easy for some items: for example, the cost of x square metres of roofing is published and fairly predictable. It is harder for other, less tangible effects, such as the productivity gains that an option might achieve, or the cost in terms of traffic congestion or environmental pollution of additional journey times to a new location. In such cases there may be little by way of published data to rely on, and little agreement as to definitions. There is a choice as to whether costs are limited to costs to the organisation, or considered more widely including, say, environmental costs. How should the money value of meeting an organisation's objectives for welfare and the environment be assessed? This is ultimately a matter of judgement, and such judgements are a weakness of the technique, as they are open to manipulation by those with an axe to grind. Used dispassionately and professionally, cost–benefit analysis is a useful technique, but it is hardly an exact science.

The effects of the choice of an option occur over time, and that time is likely to be the life of the building, though shorter timeframes may be set if clients need to see a positive return within a much shorter period. Selecting the timeframe is crucial to the calculation, as it affects and can determine the attractiveness of options.

There is a seven-step process:[5]

1 Determine the objectives.

2 Agree how widely to define the effects – the costs and benefits of the project.

3 Define money values for each effect.

4 Set a timeframe.

5 Discount the value of effects to their present value.

6 Evaluate the options.

7 Select a preferred option.

8.2.6 Net present value

Step 5 listed above (discounting to net present value) is necessary because the value of a sum of money at some time in the future will be less than its value today. In order to have sums that are comparable, they are compared at the same point in time, usually the present. The conversion is made using tables that show the present value of £1 at various times in the future, given certain assumptions.[6] In choosing which table to use, a judgement is made as to the likely average interest rate available to the clients over the period, and the probable rate of inflation. Once the variables have been defined, a lifetime cost for each option is calculated and compared. The relevant tables are as follows:

- The *amount of £1 table* shows the sum that will be produced at a point in the future for £1 invested now.
- The *present value (PV) of £1 table* shows the sum that, if invested today, would produce the sum of £1 at a specified point in time: that is, the reciprocal of the amount table.

Example

It is estimated that the interior of a building will require new floor finishes in 6 years' time. What sum, if invested now at 6.5%, will produce the £25,000 needed for replacement in 6 years? Using table or specialist software, the answer is £17,133.

- The *amount of £1 per annum table* shows the sum that will be produced at points in the future for £1 invested each year for a specified period.
- The *annual sinking fund (ASF) table* gives the amount to be invested each year to produce a fixed sum at a point in the future.
- The *year's purchase (YP) single rate table* gives the sum that, if invested today, would produce £1 annually for a defined number of years.

Example

It is predicted that option A for a heating and cooling installation will cost £250 a year in cleaning and maintenance over the expected 10 years of its life to replacement. What sum should be invested now to provide an annual sum of £250, at 6.5%

interest over 10 years? Using tables or specialist software, the answer is £1,797.

Additional tables provide for:

- the effect of two percentage rates, as for instance interest both on the sum invested and on the ASF
- the effect of tax rate
- *reversion to perpetuity*, giving values for payments that continue without fixed period, such as rents in long leases

8.2.7 Investment and development appraisals

In the context of commercial development, the developer calculates the balances of the costs of investment against the returns. The aim is to calculate whether developing a building or site will produce a commercial rate of return on the investment with an acceptable level of risk. In investment appraisal, the return on investment is compared with costs of capital, borrowing and taxation over a specified period of time. The aim is to establish the maximum budget that the project could viably support. Development appraisal considers the value of the completed product against the cost of land, construction and professional fees. This is usually done on the basis of an outline design proposal, but could equally be based on a costed building brief. The briefing consultant will probably not be called upon to carry out these calculations, but it is as well to understand the context within which a developer client will be working. These two appraisals are the commercial equivalent of the strategic brief, described in Chapter 2.

8.2.8 Risk

One could say that one of the prime functions of briefing is to assist in managing the risks that a building will not suitable be for its purpose, that an investment is unwise, or the timing is too late. Without a brief there is uncertainty as to what is to be built, at what cost, and when. Briefing is a process of identifying uncertainties and thereby converting them to risks that are amenable to management. An unidentified problem is obviously unmanageable in a way that an identified problem is not.

All investment is a risk because the future is unknowable, but there are some general rules for risk taking, which apply however sophisticated the risk analysis:[7]

- Don't risk a lot for a little.
- Never risk more than you can afford to lose; never endanger core operations.
- Always plan ahead.

- Always analyse both the source and the consequences of a risk.
- Consider the controllable and the uncontrollable parts of the risk.
- Consider the odds, and what experience and intuition tell one.
- Always have an alternative way as a contingency plan.
- Don't assume that all will go according to plan; ask 'What happens if...?'
- Don't use other people as excuses for inaction.
- Don't take risks for reasons of principle or to avoid losing face.
- Be prepared to seek the advice of experts.

In briefing, some of the risks to be managed are:

- misunderstanding scope, cost and time – the purpose of the brief is to get this right, and the risk can be reduced if not wholly avoided by client reviews of the draft
- investment risk, the risk that a required return will not be realised on the investment – usually a problem for the developer rather than the briefing consultant
- unforeseen changes in operations, often because of technological change, even before occupancy
- the risk of being misled by informants within the client organisation
- risks associated with building resilience, providing for business continuity, as discussed in Chapter 10
- the risk that the purpose of the project will be removed by events over which neither clients nor consultant have control, such as a company takeover or a collapsing market
- legal risks – risks that in some way the project will fall foul of the law or incur legal liability
- risks associated with statutory authorities – for instance that planning permission will be problematic
- risks associated with quality assurance – the briefing consultant or design team being unable to complete the work on time because of inadequate procedures, management, or insufficient skilled personnel, etc.

Risks fall into two categories: controllable and uncontrollable. *Controllable risks* include those that can be prevented by foresight, by negotiation, or by paying someone else to take the risk, such as a contractor or insurance company. The briefing consultant should consider what risks he or she is implicitly taking over from the client and covering with professional indemnity insurance. *Uncontrollable risks* include unexpected changes to regulations, and exceptionally severe weather.

Risks can be classified very simply by the likelihood that they will occur, say on a scale of 1 to 5 between very unlikely and very likely, and against severity, on a scale of costs running between negligible and disastrous. These two dimensions form the axes of a matrix for deciding how to manage identified risks.

Other techniques include:

- *portfolio management* – not putting all one's investment eggs in one basket
- *sensitivity analysis* – examining the effects on the viability of the project as each variable is given increased or decreased values (for instance, 'what if' the project takes increasingly longer to complete, or cost progressively increases)
- *scenario analysis* – examining and comparing the effects of a series of 'what if' situations

Where good historic data are available, the statistical probabilities of adverse events occurring can be calculated, probably by a specialist consultant. There is also sophisticated dependency modelling software available for analysing risk, which again requires specialist training to use, but is very powerful in situations where operations are valuable and clearly definable, and judgements can be made of the probability of adverse events.[8]

8.2.9 Value management

In describing briefing, emphasis has been placed on defining the requirements that will support activities. The idea behind value management is that not only are requirements satisfied by conceptual solution and design, but they are satisfied in the most cost-effective way. That is, the scope and quality should be no better than is necessary to meet the requirements, and certainly no more costly. Proposed solutions are assessed for economy, bearing in mind the requirements. Are there less costly ways of meeting the objectives they support? This test can be applied at each stage of briefing and design, and at each level of scale, from region, through to single building, fitting out and building components.

It is also important to consider requirements for facilities in the light of operations. Sometimes minor operational changes can reduce requirements and building costs. Sometimes an additional capital investment will reduce long-term operating costs and the lifetime cost of the project. Cost–benefit analysis will be applied in each case. Value management should not be seen simply as a cost-cutting exercise.

There is a deeper level to value management that has developed sophisticated tools for adding value to projects and to the process of which the building project is a part. Values will usually be expressed in monetary terms but, in addition to profitability, they can also include values for quality, for ethical or community goals, and for the environment.[9] As a team decision-making process it has the following advantages:

- It enables 'stakeholders' who may come from different disciplines to communcate and make common project decisions.
- It provides methods for selecting preferred options.
- It integrates the business case argument into decisions about how to achieve objectives.
- It includes functional analysis, which determines why and how actions should be taken to achieve agreed objectives (FAST).
- It is amenable to employment at various levels of scale.
- It distinguishes between long-term and short-term objectives and decisions, and gives each its place.

It is quite that, for all except the smallest of projects, the next generation of briefing technique may develop in conjunction with value engineering method.

1   For further reading on the area of the economics of operating buildings, see B. Williams' excellent book, *Facilities Economics, Incorporating Premises Audits*, Building Economics Bureau, Bromley, 1996. Though focused on office buildings, the priciples apply to most building types.
2   One of the best sources of initial cost information is the *Quarterly Review of Building Prices*, produced by Building Cost Information Services Ltd, which is owned by the RICS and is available by subscription. See www.bcis.co.uk. Price books are also produced annually by Spon, Laxton and Ti Wessex.
3   The Building Research Establishment has a Centre of Whole Life Performance, which offers consultancy advice: www.bre.co.uk.
4   R. Flanagan et al. *Life Cycle Costing*, Blackwell Scientific, Oxford, 1989.
5   A. Ashworth, *Cost Studies of Buildings*, Addison Wesley Longman Ltd, Harlow, 1999.
6   A.W. Davidson, *Parry's Valuation and Investment Tables*, 1989. See also www.boe-systems.co.uk for Valtab free calculation software.
7   R. Flanagan and G. Norman *Risk Management and Construction*, Blackwell Scientific, Oxford, 1993.
8   For dependency modelling software see e.g. www.ariumtech.com
9   For further information on value management, see www.brookes.ac.uk/other/veamac, which contains useful links and a bibliography. The Building Research Establishment has a site on this subject at www.hekios.bre.co.uk/valman

9 Statement of need and option appraisal

This chapter gives checklists for statement of need – the clients' own first efforts to define what is required in the proposed new space. It also discusses option appraisal, in which options are identified and tested. Further discussion of the place of these procedures is provided in Chapter 2. These procedures will be carried out fully and formally in large projects, and may be dealt with informally in a few short sentences in very small projects.[1] Questions to be asked at each of these stages are summarised in the checklists in Table 9.1.

Table 9.1 Checklist for statement of need and option appraisal

Statement of need		
9.1.1	Purpose of this report	• To whom is this report addressed, and what decision is requested?
9.1.2	Purpose of the project	• Why is this briefing study being conducted?
9.1.3	Role	• What is the role of the user organisation?
9.1.4	Organisational background	• What are the characteristics of the intended user organisation?
9.1.5	Policy background	• How does this project fit within the clients' policy objectives and business strategy?
9.1.6	Management context	• What management issues have led to this project?
9.1.7	Physical context	• What space does the organisation currently occupy?
9.1.8	Budget	• What is the budget, if any?
9.1.9	Time	• What are the project's major time constraints?
9.1.10	Growth and change	• What is the potential for growth and change?
9.1.11	Sustainable development	• To what extent are issues of sustainability important to the client?
9.2.1	Activities	• What operations are to be carried out in the new space?
9.2.2	Requirements	• How much space is required, and of what types?
Option appraisal		
9.3.1	Requirements	• What activities will the new space support?
9.3.2	Analysis of requirements	• What features are required of the new space?
9.3.3	Identification of options	• What options are available for meeting the requirements?
9.3.4	Testing the options	• What are the global costs of the option and the value of its benefits?
9.3.5	Approval of the preferred option	• Which option is preferred and proposed for approval?

9.1 Statement of need, role and context

9.1.1 Purpose of this report

Here the consultant states to whom the report is addressed, and what action is requested in response.

9.1.2 Purpose of the project

- What is the overall aim of this briefing study?
- What more detailed objectives have been defined, to solve what problems,

under what major constraints?
• What are the most important two or three issues relating to this project?

9.1.3 Role

The role statement is a short statement of the aim, purpose, role or mission of the occupying organisation, department or workgroup – what it is for. (See Chapter 1.)

9.1.4 Organisational background

What are the characteristics of the organisation that will occupy the new space, its age, size, structure, annual turnover and capitalisation?

• What is its size and recent history?
• What are its specialities, its strengths and its weaknesses?
• What is its standing in its market sector?
• Who are its competitors?

9.1.5 Policy background

The policy level involves the aim and objectives of the organisation and its business strategy.

• What is the overall business strategy for the organisation?
• What is the facilities strategy that has been developed from the business plan, if any?
• What developments or changes in policy necessitate the present project?

9.1.6 Management context

• What management issues have led to this project?
• What management changes make it necessary, and what changes might it generate?
• How will changes in policy be implemented through changes in working practices and staff deployment?
• Are there other management changes taking place that are relevant to the briefing process?

9.1.7 Physical context

- What space does the organisation currently occupy?
- How much area?
- Where, what locations?
- Are these freehold or leasehold?
- What are the dates of lease breaks and lease ends?
- What are the area, type and condition of each building?
- Are there any special characteristics of buildings or sites?
- What are the constraints and opportunities of the existing buildings and sites?
- If there is a proposed site or sites, what are their sizes and key characteristics?

9.1.8 Budget

- Is there a target budget, and if so what is it?
- Is the budget a fixed given sum, or are the clients looking to consultants for advice?
- If the budget has been fixed, on what basis was that done?
- Are the clients open to a discussion of budget in relation to value, or is initial capital expenditure the sole criterion?
- If yes, are the clients prepared to work with costs on the basis of whole life?
- Are they prepared to consider value over time or only initial capital costs? (See Chapter 8.)

9.1.9 Time

On a large project a major timetabling exercise will form part of briefing and feasibility studies. At this stage the aim is to understand the major time constraints from the clients' viewpoint. The programme will be developed and tested as the scope of the project is clarified.

- What are the project's major time constraints?

9.1.10 Growth and change

- What potential forces make for growth and change in use, market forces, technological or other change?

9.1.11 Sustainable development

- To what extent are the clients committed to implementing measures for environmental sustainability?

At this stage they relate to selecting a location, to siting and to overall design and cost. (See Chapter 5 for a discussion of the implications.)

9.2 Statement of need, activities and requirements

9.2.1 Activities

- What operations are to be carried out in the new space?
- How, broadly, will they be organised, and what are their key features?
- How many staff and visitors will use the space?
- What materials will be processed in the space? How will they arrive and leave, and what waste will be produced?

9.2.2 Requirements

- Roughly how much space is required?
- How will people and goods arrive at and leave the space or site?
- What are the clients' objectives for quality, image and appearance?
- Are there any unusual structural or architectural features required?
- What are the clients' more specific objectives for sustainable development in design and construction?
- Broadly to what extent and for what range of purposes is the building required to support growth and change?
- How long is the new space required to last in terms of structure, services infrastructure and internal finishes?

9.3 Option appraisal

9.3.1 Analysing activities

What activities will the new space support? More detail may be required to expand the description of activities and operations that the new space will accommodate. If necessary, details can be drawn from the fuller activity checklist in Chapter 10.

Here the considerations are:

- looking at options for redesigning activities to achieve the objectives at lower cost, by using existing space more intensively, and simplifying or omitting some activities completely (can existing resources be used more effectively or intensively while maintaining an appropriate level of quality?)
- examining possibilities for contracting out some functions, so as to remove requirements from the site
- examining the viability of employing new technologies to automate suitable functions
- asking whether it is feasible to employ the clean technology approach described in Chapter 5 to design out unnecessary activity and especially the production of waste materials

9.3.2 Analysing requirements

What features are required of the new space? Each of the options for operational organisation defined above will have differing requirements for serviced space. Which operational options require standard facilities and which require additional or reduced space or features? Requirements should be quantified wherever possible following some of the headings in the facilities guidelines and requirements sections of Chapters 10 and 11.

9.3.3 Identifying the options

What options are available for meeting the requirements? From the work done in the previous two sections, a number of possible options will emerge. If there are more than about four, it may be necessary to assess each before focusing on the most promising few, rarely more than four. Each option is described briefly, together with its implications for operations. There is always the option of doing nothing, and its implications are also considered for comparison. In some cases it will be the best course.

9.3.4 Testing the options

What are the global costs of each option and the value of its benefits? Cost–benefit analysis is described in Chapter 8.

- Which option offers the best value, including both tangible and intangible values and costs?
- Is the argument for each option accurate and internally consistent?

- Will the proposed space fit on the available site or within the available building?
- Is the proposed space affordable, in terms of both initial capital expenditure and whole life costs, and what will these costs be?
- Is the business case for the option convincing?
- Is the investment risk acceptable?
- Is the expenditure consistent with the organisation's policy objectives and facilities plan?
- Can the project be built in the required time?
- Is there any need to phase or zone construction, or decant functions temporarily, and is this feasible?
- Is the new space buildable and durable?
- Is the construction risk acceptable, and can it be mitigated?
- Are the construction health and safety risks acceptable?
- Does the option meet the clients' sustainable development objectives, especially at this stage for the choice of site or location, including:
    - impacts on the local community
    - impacts on transport systems and sustainable transport policies
    - complementing or enhancing the surroundings and local landmarks
    - impact on existing plants, wildlife and water resources
    - use of brown land rather than greenfield sites
    - generation of solid and liquid waste products, water- and airborne, and pollution
- Is the option in all its particulars consistent with best practice for operations within its category?
- Are the statutory consents required to construct and operate the option likely to be achievable?
- Can the option meet the clients' objectives for image, quality and appearance, and provide an appropriate environment for staff, other users and the public?

9.3.5 Approving the preferred option

Which option is preferred and proposed for approval? The results of the testing stage are compared, and a preferred option is recommended to the clients' senior management group for approval. Approval will be based on the project description, project cost, and business case. Following approval, the client will require advice on procurement strategy, and a strategic brief will be prepared.

---

1 This chapter is based in part on the method described in Construction Industry Board booklet, F. Duffy (ed.), *Briefing The Team*, Thomas Telford, London, 1997.

10 Building brief

This chapter consists of an annotated checklist for a brief for building design. It also includes information for a brief for a campus design: that is, design for a group of related buildings usually – but not necessarily – on a single site. In the procurement process for larger and publicly funded projects, it follows the option appraisal and strategic brief stages and precedes design and construction.[1] Some of the information produced during these previous stages, should it be available, will inform answers in this checklist. Issues concerning the procurement route should have been agreed during the strategic brief stage, and are not included in this checklist. The procurement decision will have an impact on the conduct of briefing and the readership of the brief document. It may be that the prime contractor or project manager will have a major input into the brief.

Chapter 11 gives a checklist for briefing for detailed fitting-out, which on larger projects can be carried out as a separate exercise during the building design. On smaller projects the two tasks can be carried out simultaneously and the checklists combined. The checklist has been developed to cover all conceivable circumstances, and will need to be edited to suit the characteristics of the particular project. It is summarised in Table 10.1.

The first three sections are based on answers received during interviews and meetings with a client briefing group. Written information and surveys may also be helpful.

The last two sections define standards and objectives to be met by the design, and are developed by the consultant in response to the activity description and in consultation with the clients and users.

10.1 Context

The context section confirms and expands on the statement of need and option appraisal documents described in the Chapter 9 checklist. Unless very recent, the statement of need, option appraisal and strategic brief are reviewed, confirmed and used to provide the context for a building brief. If those steps have not been completed, it is advisable to go back and retrace them before proceeding with the building brief.

Table 10.1 Checklist for project brief: brief for campus design and building design

Context

10.1	Context	• Why is this briefing being conducted?

Role

10.2.1	Role statement	• What is the role, aim, purpose or mission of the occupying organisation?
10.2.2	Policy objectives	• What specific objectives are there within the role statement?
10.2.3	Parameters	• What is the relationship in terms of role between this organisation, department or workgroup and others?
10.2.4	Culture	• How can the culture of the user organisation be defined?
10.2.5	Growth and change	• What is the likelihood of change within the organisation?
10.2.6	Sustainable development	• What is the clients' policy on sustainable development?
10.2.7	Managing sustainability	• What strategy and plans are there for managing sustainability?
10.2.8	Location and site	• What are the implications of location and site development for sustainability?
10.2.9	Image and appearance	• What is the clients' policy for image and appearance?

Activities

10.3.1	Activities	• What operations are to be carried out in the new space?
10.3.2	Organisational structure	• How is the organisation structured into departments?
10.3.3	Staff	• What staff will work in the new space?
10.3.4	Visitors	• In addition to staff, who visits the site or sites?
10.3.5	Materials	• What materials are used in day-to-day activities?
10.3.6	Flow	• What are the major flows between functions on the site?
10.3.7	Time	• What are the time cycle characteristics of activities?
10.3.8	Management issues	• What are the key relevant management issues?
10.3.9	Growth and change	• What, in detail, is the potential for growth and change?

Facility guidelines

10.4.1	Transport	• How do materials, staff and visitors arrive at the site?
10.4.2	Internal circulation	• What are the generators of circulation routes within the building?
10.4.3	Zoning	• How should functions be grouped on the site or separated?
10.4.4	Security	• What security precautions are required?
10.4.5	Resilience	• What levels of resilience are appropriate for business continuity?
10.4.6	Structural features	• What requirements are there for exceptional building forms?
10.4.7	Image, quality and appearance	• What requirements are there for image, quality, or appearance?
10.4.8	Site planning brief	• Are there any specific planning objectives?
10.4.9	Growth and change	• What guidelines are appropriate for growth and change?
10.4.10	Land use	• What guidelines are appropriate for land use?
10.4.11	Energy use	• What guidelines are appropriate for energy use?
10.4.12	Pollution	• What guidelines are appropriate for pollution control?
10.4.13	Water management	• What guidelines are appropriate for water management?
10.4.14	Materials	• What guidelines are appropriate for the selection of construction materials?
10.4.15	Design for sustainability	• What guidelines are appropriate in designing for sustainability?
10.4.16	Health and safety	• Are guidelines required additional to the statutory minimum?
10.4.17	Site utilities strategies	• Are guidelines required for site utilities provision?
10.4.18	Building services strategies	• What guidelines are appropriate for building services?
10.4.19	Budget	• What are the budget guidelines?
10.4.20	Programme	• What are the programme guidelines?

Facility requirements

10.5.1	Space list	• What spaces are required, and what are their areas?
10.5.2	Relationships between spaces: single building	• What are the required proximities between spaces?
10.5.3	Area allocation and budget for a campus	• What are the facilities, areas and budget?
10.5.4	Interior environment: single building	• What are the requirements for the internal environment generally?
10.5.5	Element data sheets: single building	• What are the specific requirements for groups of spaces?

10.2 Role

10.2.1 Role statement

- What is the role, aim, purpose or mission of the occupying organisation?

The idea of role was discussed in Chapter 1. The role statement is a short statement of the aim, purpose, role or mission of the occupying organisation, department or workgroup – what it is for. From it flow a number of policy objectives, which are considered within this section.

10.2.2 Policy objectives

- What specific objectives, markers or measures have been defined within the overall aim of the role statement?
- How will the success of the overall aim be measured?
- What more detailed policies are required to implement it?

Example

Objectives may include restructuring the organisation to form new departments with new responsibilities, in pursuit of the aim. Alternatively, an objective may be to increase sales by 10% by a specific date, to consolidate production at a single location in order to make savings, or to make changes that save money, improve environmental sustainability and enhance the organisation's image.

10.2.3 Parameters

Parameters are the borders or edges of the clients' operations compared with those of other similar organisations.

- What is the relationship, in terms of role, between this organisation, department or workgroup and others?
- What is its role in relation to a network of similar operations and to the local or regional plan?

Examples

- What is the relationship between a university and other nearby academic and research institutions?
- What is the relationship between a medical practice, local hospitals and other health care services?

- What is the relationship between a branch office, other branch offices, and head office?
- How is *this* organisation differentiated from its competitors?

10.2.4 Culture

How can the culture of the user organisation be defined? Every large organisation has a culture that governs the style in which work is done and the unspoken rules for behaviour. At the scale of a campus it is sufficient to understand the organisation's traditions and intentions. At the scale of a single building more detail is required. Culture reaches into working practices and personal interactions at every level. Some organisations are very aware of this and consciously develop a culture that reinforces their business plan objectives. For instance, staff dress code, lines of communication, training in teamwork, training in dealing with customers, product design, information technology, interior design, environmental policy, marketing strategy, brand image and advertising will all be coordinated to deliver business plan objectives. Other organisations are less aware and have perhaps inherited patterns of work and interaction that are no longer appropriate. Organisational culture may be difficult to perceive from within an organisation, but easier for a trained outside observer. Here are a few pointers:

- Is the management structure vertically hierarchical or based on cooperation laterally between people with specialist functions?
- Do communications go up to the head of department, across to the head of another department, and down to the appropriate person, or do they go directly to the person in other departments regardless of status?
- Where do staff eat lunch? Is there any catering provision? Are there separate dining rooms for various staff grades, or a common cafeteria?
- What staff amenities are available?
- Is there a sense of cooperation between departments with a common aim
- of completing the present project, or a lack of cooperation and defence of territory and status?
- Has the organisation gained quality management or environmental management certification?
- Do the clients acknowledge the consultant's report on the culture as realistic?
- Is the culture consistent with the role?
- Could improvements in culture be made that increase the effectiveness of the organisation?
- If so, what, with what objective, how, at what cost, when, and with what implications for the present project?

10.2.5 Growth and change

What is the likelihood of change within the organisation? One can safely assume that every organisation is in a constant state of change, whether resulting from market forces, changes in people's perceived needs, or technological change.

- What is the strategy for the medium-term and long-term future of the organisation?
- What are the contingency plans if the organisation is more or less successful than projected by say 15%?
- What would be the implications for each of the objectives in this section in either case?

10.2.6 Sustainable development

What is the clients' policy on sustainable development? The issue of sustainable development, as discussed in Chapter 5, flows from the clients' organisational policy. The level of policy commitment to sustainable development and operations will result in benchmarks and targets in the brief below, and in planned regular monitoring and attention to those targets following occupancy. This section (role) is the place to set out the clients' overall policies:

- Do the clients have a written policy on sustainable development?
- If so, how is the policy to be translated into action? Which of the following approaches most closely describes the clients' position:
  - Conform to legal requirements and regulations
  - As above, but adopt sustainable solutions where savings can be shown in initial costs
  - As above, but adopt solutions where cost savings can be shown in initial and operating costs over 2 years, 5 years, 10 years, or long term
  - The new construction and the operations it accommodates will be exemplary[2] in terms of sustainable development, at an additional initial cost of 2%, 5%, 10% or more over the cost of conventional development.

10.2.7 Managing sustainability

- What strategy and plans are there for managing sustainability?
- Who is in charge of developing environmental policies?
- Who is in charge of setting targets, implementing and monitoring them?
- What monitoring is being done in relation to existing buildings and operations?
- What targets have been set for energy use, wastewater reduction or recycling,

airborne emissions, internal environmental standards, building user satisfaction, solid waste reduction, etc.?

10.2.8 Location and site

What are the implications of location and site development for sustainability? There are costs attached to decisions in the areas listed below, and there are limits to the control that developers have over some of the issues raised, especially on smaller projects. However, an initial commitment and determination to tackle some of these issues, when carried through into detailed briefing and design, will make a great difference to the final outcome.

- Has a site been selected for the new construction? If not, has redesigning operations so that additional space is not required been considered as an option, involving:
  - redefining the concept of the service or product provided
  - changing operational methods
  - contracting out certain functions
  - adopting new technologies
  - extending an existing building
  - leasing additional space
  - renovating a newly purchased building
  - using a brownfield rather than a greenfield site
- Is it the clients' policy to develop the proposed site so as to improve, and at least not degrade:
  - the visual quality of the surroundings
  - local traffic pollution and congestion
  - the quality of local water resources and watershed systems
  - local and on-site wildlife habitat and planting
  - minimisation of waste and pollution, airborne, waterborne, liquid and solid
  - in larger projects, cultural, amenity and employment opportunities for the local community
  - health and safety and environmental quality for staff, visitors and the local community
  - respect for landscape features and local landmarks, both manmade and natural
- In the case of large projects, will the local community be involved in comment and discussion during briefing and design, beyond the statutory minimum?
- Will steps be taken to control noise, waste generation, traffic, water, and other pollution during construction?

10.2.9 Image and appearance

What is the policy for image and appearance? The way an organisation wishes to present itself to the public will be reflected in its buildings. This will be done consciously in organisations concerned with a brand image, where buildings may be tied in with marketing exercises. There is also a relationship with the culture of the organisation because, regardless of design, advertising and other branding features, the way people communicate with each other within the organisation will be reflected in communications with customers and the public.

10.3 Activities

This section is concerned with *what people do*, rather than the requirements for the buildings or other facilities needed to support them. If every user organisation, even a family, has a role or purpose, then the things that people do are generally in fulfilment of that role, and more specifically so in a commercial or publicly funded organisation.

What people do now may not be what they will do in the new space, so it is worth questioning the general organisation of operations and how activities may change. There will be many cases where it is not possible to do this except in a general way, either because operations and technologies are changing fast, or because the end user is not known. Working through the activities section gives an opportunity to redesign operations, to consider ways of using space more intensively, or to use technological developments to design out certain functions altogether. With planning, this can be done while maintaining or improving quality and reliability. Finally, it may be possible to use the clean technology approach, described in Chapter 5, to minimise or substantially avoid the production of waste materials and pollution.

10.3.1 Activities

- What operations are carried out?
- What is the primary function of the site as a whole and of each department or, at the single building level, each workgroup?
- What services are provided in the building, or what products are manufactured or distributed?
- Are there any special or atypical activities?
- What are the core activities on which the survival of the organisation depends, as opposed to support activities?

10.3.2 Organisational structure

An organisation chart is useful here.

- How is the organisation structured into departments?

10.3.3 Staff

What staff will work in the new space? In a brief for a group of buildings, at the campus level, it may be sufficient to know how many staff will be employed in each department. At the building level, more information is required. Staff numbers should be listed by department and workgroup. This may seem simple, but it usually requires some investigation, as staff on the human resources department complement may not tally with those on the accounts department payroll. These are some categories of staff that may be missed:

- part time staff
- home-workers
- staff based elsewhere
- staff who travel much of the time
- external contractors and consultants who need work space on site
- seasonal and temporary staff paid through agencies
- staff positions that have been authorised but not filled
- positions where staff have left and will not be replaced
- positions requested by departments but not yet authorised

In a large organisation it is wise to agree some broad rules to simplify the way in which staff numbers are arrived at.

How can staff be categorised by function? Many organisations still categorise staff by how much they earn rather than by what they do.

Having established current staffing, how are numbers and organisation likely to change over the next two time periods? One may look at 2 years and 5 years, or 5 years and 10 years, depending on the situation.

- What has been the record over the last 5 years?
- Is there a discrepancy between stated future figures and figures reached by projecting the historic record forward? If so, what are the reasons for this?
- How will staff numbers be affected if the organisation is more or less successful by 15%?

Through these exercises it is possible to arrive at high, low and median staff projections as the basis for briefing, and to develop strategies for dealing with these variations.

10.3.4 Visitors

In addition to staff, who visits the site or sites? On larger projects, surveys will be required to establish or forecast numbers and categories of visitors.
- How many people visit?
- Which departments are visited, and for what purposes?
- How can visitors be categorised, and what are the characteristics of each category? Categorisation may be by age, those with children, various disabilities, socio-economic group, visitors on business or receiving services, etc.

Examples
Customers in a shop, patients at a surgery, clients at a professional office, people at an airport.

10.3.5 Materials

- What materials are used in day-to-day operations?
- What are the raw materials or products that come into the functional system of the building, and the finished products and wastes that leave it?
- What are their characteristics and quantities?
- How are they used?
- How do products and waste leave the site and each department or building?
- Which departments require these goods and materials, and for what purposes?
- How can waste be minimised, recycled as a useful material or designed out of the process?
- Do all materials come from renewable or sustainable sources and, if not, are they replaceable by substitution or redesign?
- Are all materials safe, non-toxic and non-polluting and, if not, are they replaceable? How will any toxicity or pollution be managed?

10.3.6 Flow

What are the major destinations and major flows between functions on the site? On some projects a flow diagram will communicate the principles of flow through the site and between departments. (See Chapter 7 for an explanation of flow diagrams.)

- How do staff, visitors, members of the public, cars, buses, trucks, materials of various types, etc. arrive at and pass through the site?
- How can pollution and congestion be minimised, for instance by incentives to use less damaging modes of transport?
- At the campus level, what are the key priorities for circulation?
- At the building level, how do these various flows arrive at and pass between departments or workgroups?
- What flows require priority because of volume of traffic or importance?

10.3.7 Time

- What are the time cycle characteristics of the life of the organisation and of its activities?
- Are there critical daily cycles – weekly, monthly, seasonal, annual?

Examples
- At the campus scale: seasonal peaks in an airport; twice daily rush-hours as staff arrive for work and leave a business park.
- At the building scale: seasonal peaks in a hotel; daily cycles in patient care on a hospital ward; a daily cycle of assessing credit status and responding to loan requests in a lending organisation.

10.3.8 Management issues

What are the key relevant management issues awaiting resolution, and what are the options for resolution? 'Management' is used here to describe the arrangement and control of day-to-day operations, as opposed to policy, which is strategic and is described in the Role section.

10.3.9 Growth and change

What, in detail, is the potential for growth and change? Change is one of the few certainties. The business plan is unlikely to be precisely realised. The brief envisages a range of situations, which approximate to what will actually happen. It is very probable that in some areas the unforeseeable will happen. What will be the impact on activities of the following:

- growth or decrease in throughput of work
- growth or decrease in staff numbers, as discussed above
- changes in the market, customer demand, competition

- changes in ownership and organisation
- proposed or probable changes in legislation or government policy
- known or probable changes in technology?

It is often useful to check with best practice in the industry and review the relevant trade press to understand the potential for changes in technology and management approach.

- Are particular functions or departments more likely to change than others? If so, which ones, how and within what range?

In the testing stage, a number of scenarios are developed that model solutions to the range of probabilities defined in this section of the brief. The aim is to create solutions that are robust and adaptable, whatever the change.

10.4 Facility guidelines[3]

Whereas the Activities section describes *what people do* in the organisation, this section and the requirements that follow define *design guidelines* for a single building or a campus – a group of related buildings.

10.4.1 Transport

- What are the ways in which people, materials, goods and information arrive at and leave the building?
- What means of transport will be used to access the site, and by how many people?
- What are the numbers of people, and numbers and types of vehicles – for example staff cars, visitors' cars, buses, trucks and delivery vans of various sizes, garbage trucks, parking?
- How will deliveries of goods and materials be handled? What types of transport are involved, and in what quantities?
- What circulation routes will enable people, goods and materials to move between facilities on a campus site?
- What implications are there for access, drop-off areas, loading and parking?

10.4.2 Internal circulation

- What are the generators of circulation routes through the building?
- What are the major flows for people, materials and objects through

the building?

- What are the major destinations within the building?
- What are seen as the entrance points, reception, shipping/receiving functions, together with perimeter security checkpoints?
- Are any internal transport systems envisaged, such as conveyer belts, pneumatic tubes, lifts, escalators, cart systems or mail distribution, and what are their characteristics?
- What are the major communications systems envisaged for the building, such as cabling of various types for data and voice, cellular and satellite communications?

10.4.3 Zoning

What are the special requirements for grouping departments or functions on the site or separating them:

- by convenience for visitor access
- by security-controlled access for specific categories of people
- by functional category
- by requirements for closeness between departments
- by the generation of noise or other hazards
- by transport or other access requirements
- by special servicing requirements
- by other characteristics?

10.4.4 Security

What security precautions are required? In large organisations or those with particular sensitivity, a formal security risk assessment will be required. This will look at the security hazards and risks, both internal and from external sources, taking into account the nature of operations and the characteristics of the neighbourhood.

- What are the security risks, probabilities and possible effects on the organisation and its operations?
- What are the security risks particular to the site and neighbourhood?
- What are the security risks to specific buildings and other facilities?
- What types and levels of security are appropriate for the site and buildings?
- Is any internal security zoning required?
- Are there any other special site security issues?

10.4.5 Resilience

What levels of resilience are appropriate, and what risks are they required to protect against? Resilience concerns the measures taken to avoid or mitigate threats to the continuity of operations. Such threats may come from breaches of security, whether internal or from outside. Equally disruptive can be extreme weather, floods, power failures, fire, or loss of access to the building because of events close by, outside the control of the client. As with many of the items in the checklist, there is a choice between designing to normally accepted good practice by conforming to statutory regulations, or going beyond these to provide additional levels of resilience. Regulations are designed to protect life and prevent injury, but additional precautions may be necessary to, say, protect valuable documents. Planning for resilience, or business continuity, involves a process of assessing risks and reviewing operational procedures as well requirements to upgrade the physical resilience of the building.[4] If the worst happens, insurance will provide a sum of money, but that alone will not necessarily save a business that depends on uninterrupted operations.

If measures are thought necessary, the process involves:

- identifying the hazard
- using records where possible, calculating or estimating the probability of its occurrence
- assessing the severity of its effects
- defining guidelines or requirements to avoid or mitigate those effects
- ensuring that a budget is allocated, commensurate with the risk and potential harm

Example
Following an assessment, it was decided, in an office building, that no wet services would run over or through spaces equipped with computer networks in order to avoid damage caused by leaks.

10.4.6 Structural features

Are there functions requiring exceptional building forms that immediately stand out:

- especially long clear spans
- unusually high floor-to-ceiling clearances
- areas with special load-bearing capacities?

10.4.7 Image, quality and appearance

- Do the clients have any preconceptions of the style or quality of building?
- Are there any words that would capture the clients' intentions?
- What degree of latitude is permitted to the design architect in interpreting these guidelines?
- Do the clients have any particular fixed preferences for detailed features to be included, and for what reasons?

Clients may need help in articulating their intentions and testing the feasibility of their preconceptions. The semantic scale technique described in Chapter 6 may be useful. A collection of illustrations or targeted building visits are helpful. Visualisations can be prepared to test the implications of these guidelines. Sometimes clients are content to leave design to the design architect.

10.4.8 Site planning brief

Are there any specific planning objectives? These will be tested by site analysis and feasibility studies:

- Does the client have any specific constraints or objectives in site planning or for situating buildings on the site?
- Is a planning and urban design brief required, defining how site planning and building design fit in with surrounding sites and the neighbourhood context?

10.4.9 Growth and change

What guidelines are appropriate to allow for the possibility of future expansion, growth or change on the site or within the building? Guidelines should be defined for:

- internal adaptability. Adaptability requires a degree of spare unassigned space to allow for new functions and for decanting existing functions while space is reconfigured. Packing even the most adaptably designed building to capacity at occupancy defeats the objective.
- ensuring that heating, cooling and ventilation systems are adaptable and take into account a wide range of possible uses for the new space, not just the initial planned use
- the ability to extend particular functions, horizontally and possibly vertically
- providing demountable structures for seasonal use or occasional special requirements

• designing the building shell to withstand predicted climate changes of colder winters and hotter summers

10.4.10 Land use

What guidelines are appropriate for land use? This and the sections that follow consider what specific guidelines are necessary to implement the policies described in section 10.2.8 above. These will include design requirements to:

• complement the existing surroundings, and respect landscape features and local landmarks, both manmade or natural
• encourage the use of bicycles and, on larger projects, public transport
• maintain and enhance the quality of local water resources, and avoid additional pollution
• preserve and improve surrounding and on-site wildlife habitat and planting, starting, if appropriate, with wildlife and landscape surveys
• consider the capacity of fragile environments to support development and quantities of visitors

10.4.11 Energy use

What guidelines are appropriate for energy use in order to:

• minimise use of non-renewable energy and air-borne flue emissions? Benchmarks should be set in kWh/m^2 per year for each type of fuel and for each services function or area zone. When benchmarking and performance measurement are local and discrete it becomes much easier to understand performance and take remedial action[5]
• maximise the use of energy from renewable sources where feasible?

10.4.12 Pollution

What guidelines are appropriate for pollution avoidance and control? The measures that can be considered include:

• avoiding the use of materials that containing ozone-depleting gases, for instance in some fire-extinguishing systems, refrigerants, and insulation
• minimising the production of solid and liquid waste and especially noxious or toxic wastes
• providing defined waste storage areas and encouraging recycling schemes
• providing for composting of suitable domestic refuse

- ensuring that all types of asbestos are safely removed from any existing building or brownfield site and are disposed of appropriately
- avoiding materials that degrade the interior environment, by 'gassing out'
- avoiding materials or components that are themselves toxic or include toxic elements or treatments

10.4.13 Water management

What guidelines are appropriate for water management? The measures that can be taken include:

- minimising water use, through low-volume sanitary fittings, possibly recycling grey water and collection and use of rainwater
- minimising site water runoff
- using traps and gullies to avoid polluting site water

10.4.14 Materials

What guidelines are appropriate for the selection of construction materials? In defining selection policies, the following issues should be considered:

- using local materials, where feasible, to reduce the need for transport
- preferring materials with low embodied energy (that is, energy used in their manufacture and transport)
- using recycled materials where feasible, especially crushed masonry aggregates
- completely avoiding timber from non-sustainable resources, bearing in mind the current unreliability of certification
- using materials from renewable sources where possible
- selectively using high-performance components, especially glazing
- minimising the use of materials and products derived from fossil fuels
- using water-based paints and varnishes where appropriate

10.4.15 Design for sustainability

What guidelines are appropriate in designing for sustainability? The following areas should be particularly considered in design:

- orienting any new building for maximum exposure to sun, while providing protection from unwanted solar gain and glare
- incorporating elements of mass to stabilise temperature fluctuations

- eliminating weak points in the weatherproof envelope by a water-shedding building form and robust detailing rather than by relying on the performance of materials at their limits
- providing a building shell that is durable and requires low maintenance
- providing a building that is adaptable to future, unforeseen uses
- designing for the possibility of future extension
- optimising the provision of thermal insulation to reduce fuel consumption
- controlling air infiltration through the external envelope
- designing for low energy consumption (an appropriate benchmark should be provided in kWh/m^2 per year[6])
- maximising the use of natural ventilation where possible
- optimising the use of natural daylighting, where possible
- using energy from renewable sources, where feasible
- on larger projects, zoning services for more sensitive local responsiveness

10.4.16 Health and safety

Are guidelines required in addition to the statutory minimum? For instance, measures can be taken that will substantially increase user satisfaction. The first of these is the provision or local control of the internal environment, such as heating and ventilation, and individual control of lighting.[7] Other measures have been given in sections 10.4.12 and 10.4.14 above. In addition, consideration should be given to:

- controlling glare and unwanted solar heat gain by envelope design
- controlling sound levels and sound quality for quietness
- designing for low and easy maintenance, both of finishes and of mechanical services

A building log should be provided at handover containing maintenance manuals and a planned preventive maintenance programme, even on small projects.

10.4.17 Site utilities strategies

Are guidelines required for site utilities provision? One task in the site survey will be to establish types, capacities and locations of existing or nearby utilities. On a large project:

- What are the guidelines for utilities planning or campus energy management?
- Is the use of combined heat and power feasible?

10.4.18 Building services strategies

What guidelines are appropriate for building services? For some buildings the requirements for mechanical or electrical services are key generators of the design. In general, services should support functional activities, but sometimes a key decision should be taken early, for instance whether or not to install air conditioning in certain areas, and this may be a client requirement.

10.4.19 Budget

What are the budget guidelines? A cost analysis based on the draft brief will be necessary, and may be provided by a cost consultant.

- Is there a budget?
- Is the clients' budget expectation realistic and consistent with the stated expectations for size and quality?
- Are the clients prepared to work with costs on the basis of whole life costing?
- Are they prepared to consider value over time or only initial capital costs?

10.4.20 Programme

What are the programme guidelines? A full programme analysis will be required at the testing stage. The task here is to develop the programme further and to test its feasibility.

- Does the client have title to the site? If not, the completion of legal work may well delay other activities.
- How will the various construction projects on the site be zoned and phased?
- What are the milestone dates for design, statutory approvals, tender and construction? Are these realistic, and do they allow for specialist studies within the design process, especially regarding solutions for sustainable development?
- What is the milestone date for handover and occupancy, or for various subprojects?
- Are there any other milestone dates?
- When will the various project areas of the site be made available to contractors?
- How will continuity of operations during construction be planned and assured?

This concludes the information-gathering phase of briefing.

10.5 Facility requirements

In this section, requirements are specified that 'wrap' and support the identified activities and guidelines in serviced and equipped spaces.

10.5.1 Space list

What are the spaces and their areas? For a large site or group of buildings, departments and specific major functions on the site should be listed. For a single building, spaces should be defined to support and accommodate the activities defined above.

One or more activities may take place in a single space, sometimes in defined areas within it. It is important to distinguish between a title describing the activity (what people do) and the name of the space in which that activity takes place. People are apt to miss this distinction and assume that activities are predestined to take place in the same rooms as before. Seeing this distinction frees up thinking about spatial organisation and allows simpler solutions.

Example
The activities of cooking and eating may take place in a space called the kitchen. The activity of eating may also take place in the living room or in the dining room.

In larger buildings, spaces are organised into elements and components. An element is a small group of spaces sharing close functional links. A component is a group of elements accommodating a department or function of a complex building. For instance, a laboratory, its store room and attached office may form an element. Several of these elements form a component in a building that also has office and workshop components.

10.5.2 Relationships between spaces, single building

What are the required proximities between spaces? This may not be relevant in every project, but in some buildings it will be a primary generator of design. In those projects, it will follow from the analysis of flow between functions, as described in sections 7.2, 7.3 and 7.4.

There may be whole buildings where relationships are not critical, and some office buildings are like this. Relationships can best be shown on a relationship matrix as shown in Figure 7.2.

10.5.3 Area allocation and budget for a campus

What are the facilities, areas and budget? Square metre area requirements should be defined for each department and major function. Area is seen from two viewpoints. On the one hand, the project budget will buy limited quantities of space at appropriate costs per square metre; on the other hand, defined quantities of space are necessary to accommodate the activities described above. Any discrepancies in area calculations are resolved with the client group, together with their implications for activities and budget.

10.5.4 Interior environment, single building

What are the requirements for the internal environment generally? This section defines environmental performance standards for each category of space, according to the policies outlined above. Standards are defined for the building as a whole along with any key exceptional cases for each of the following:

- daylighting ranges and controls
- artificial lighting and controls
- heating, temperature ranges
- cooling, temperature ranges
- relative humidity ranges and controls if required
- ventilation ranges and controls
- whether natural or artificial heating, cooling, and ventilation is preferred
- acoustic privacy
- acoustic quality

10.5.5 Element data sheets, single building

What are the specific requirements for small groups of spaces? For each element, listed by component, a sheet gives the following information:

- a brief description of activities to be accommodated
- categories of staff and other users, and their numbers
- special features, structure, or finishes
- special requirements for appearance and image
- major servicing requirements
- major equipment or furniture required
- notes of required relationships to other spaces or elements, confirming information given in the relationship matrix and diagram
- a diagram showing space sizes and the relationships within the element

- notes of any of the policies or guidelines defined in earlier sections of the brief that are especially relevant to this element; there is no problem with a little repetition if information appears where the design architect most needs it

For smaller buildings, data sheets may alternatively be organised as individual spaces as described in the next chapter, omitting grouping into elements and components. Element data sheets will not be necessary in some standard building types: for example, in office buildings standards are well known, and it is sufficient to state the level of quality throughout the building and any variations.

1 See Construction Industry Board booklet, F. Duffy (ed.), *Briefing The Team*, Thomas Telford, London, 1997.
2 'Exemplary' can be defined more closely against an appropriate rating system. For instance, in the case of an office building, *BREEAM 98 for Offices*, Building Research Station; *Ecological Building Criteria for Viikki*, Helsinki City Planning Department Publications, both references quoted in Energy Research Group, *A Green Vitruvius, Principles and Practice of Sustainable Architecture*, James & James, London, 1999.
3 This section draws on S. Halliday, *The Green Guide to The Architect's Job Book*, RIBA Publications, 2000, which is recommended for further reading.
4 For more detail on resilience see D. Hyams, *The Guide to Disaster Recovery Planning*, MRC, Oxford, 1993.
5 A. Leaman and W. Bordass, *Environmental Quality, The New Agenda*, BIFM Conference 1998. www.usablebuildings.co.uk
6 See *ECON 19, Energy Efficient Offices*, Building Research Establishment, 1998, www.bre.co.uk
7 A. Leaman and W. Bordass, Keeping occupants 'satisficed', *Energy and Environmental Management*, 2nd quarter 2000, pp 23–27. For more articles on this subject see www.usablebuildings.co.uk

11 Brief for detailed design

This chapter aims to be generally comprehensive, and therefore will be relevant in full only to the most demanding building types; it originates from a list compiled for hospital briefs. For smaller or less demanding projects, a suitably edited version should be created. At the same time, it may not list items that are specific to particular building types, and those items need to be added to the customised list.

The chapter is in the format of a brief document in six parts. Section 11.1 is an introduction to the briefing project, its background and context. These subjects have been covered in Chapter 10, and their presence is merely noted here. The space list, role statement and activity description are related to the building and user organisation as a whole. Sections 11.2–11.6 that follow contain space data sheets, one sheet for each space. Responses are noted only where they are relevant, otherwise the heading is simply omitted. Answers to sections 11.4, 11.5 and 11.6 are given only where the information varies from normal standards and expectations, and here one makes some assumptions as to what will be considered normal by the readership of the brief.[1] Question headings are summarised in the checklists in Table 11.1.

11.1 Introduction and summary

This part forms an introduction to the brief. The details of each heading have been described in the two preceding chapters and are not spelled out here. They are summarised in Table 11.1. This section defines requirements of the user group for their departmental space or for the building as a whole; the sections that follow describe each individual space.

11.2 Activity

This part and those that follow are presented as space data sheets, with one sheet filled out for each space.

11.2.1 Activity description

- What is the activity or activities that the space is to support?

Example

This space accommodates discussion groups in the mornings and craftwork in the afternoon. Both activities take place around tables. Activities include crafts, board games and conversation. Patients attend on medical advice, on a voluntary basis.

Table 11.1 Checklist for project brief, brief for detailed design

Introduction and summary	
11.1.1 Context	• What is the context or background of this briefing project?
11.1.2 Physical context	• What building or site has been identified for the new space?
11.1.3 Role	• What is the role of the user organisation or department?
11.1.4 Activities	• What, overall, will the user group do in the new space?
11.1.5 Space list	• What spaces have been identified, with floor areas
Space data sheets: Activities	
11.2.1 Activity description	• What is the activity or activities the space is to support?
11.2.2 Occupancy	• How many users of each category use the space?
11.2.3 Utilisation	• For what hours in the day will the space be in use?
11.2.4 Adaptability	• To what extent will the space be rearranged or expanded?
11.2.5 Access restrictions	• Is access to this space limited to a specified group?
11.2.6 Environmental health and safety	• Do activities or processes in this space give rise to known hazards?
11.2.7 Environmental sensitivity	• Are activities in this room especially sensitive to adverse environmental conditions?
Space	
11.3.1 Floor area	• What minimum floor area is required?
11.3.2 Relationships	• What are the key requirements for proximity to other spaces?
11.3.3 Enclosure	• What degree of enclosure is required?
11.3.4 Access	• What dimensions of door opening will be required?
11.3.5 Layout diagram	• Show a simple diagram of the space
11.3.6 Special structural features	• Are there any exceptional structural requirements?
Interior environment	
11.4.1 Daylight	• Is there a functional requirement for special daylighting?
11.4.2 Views	• Is there a functional requirement for views?
11.4.3 Artificial lighting	• Are there functional requirements for special lighting or controls?
11.4.4 Environmental comfort	• Are there any special functional requirements for temperature and ventilation or controls?
11.4.5 Acoustics	• Are there any functional acoustic requirements?
11.4.6 Finishes	• Are there any functional requirements for finishes?
Services	
11.5.1 Electrical power	• What are the functional requirements, within the space, for the services listed to the left?
11.5.2 Communications and IT	
11.5.3 Other low-voltage systems	
11.5.4 Water	
11.5.5 Gases	
11.5.6 Air extract	
11.5.7 Non-IT distribution systems	
Furniture and equipment	
11.6.1 Loose furniture	• List requirements and dimensions for individual items of furniture, fixtures and fittings
11.6.2 Equipment	
11.63 Fixtures	

11.2.2 Occupancy

• How many users of each category use the space?

Example

Occupancy of 18–20 patients, 1 psychiatric nurse, 3 assistants. Patients are adult psychiatric, mildly to moderately ill.

11.2.3 Utilisation

- For what hours in the day is the space in use?

Example

Weekdays from 8.30 am to 12.00 noon, and 2.00 pm to 4.30 pm. Occasional evening use to 9.00 pm.

11.2.4 Adaptability

- To what extent will the space be rearranged or expanded, and how frequently?

Example

Tables may be rearranged, but counter and storage will be fixed. Tables may be stacked for movement, exercise or dance activities each Tuesday morning. The pottery area is closed off when not in use and opened to the main space when required.

11.2.5 Access restrictions

- Is access to this space limited to a specified group?
- Should the space be contained within a defined security zone?
- If so, what degree of security is required?
- What type of security is appropriate: manned, mechanical, electronic, CCTV, centrally controlled?

Example

Access is controlled by the nurse in charge; lockable door.

11.2.6 Environmental health and safety

- Do activities or processes in this space give rise to known hazards?
- Are poisonous or noxious substances or wastes used or generated in the space?
- If not hazardous, are outputs sufficiently unpleasant to require special treatment?

Example

Clay dust from pottery; heat from kiln; flammable liquids used under close supervision and stored in regulation cabinet; noise generated by some craft and social activities; kitchen smells.

• In normal use, are special treatments required to mitigate hazards?

Example

Floor finish in pottery to mitigate slipperiness when wet.

11.2.7 Environmental sensitivity

• Are activities in this room especially sensitive to adverse environmental conditions: noise, vibration, heat, light, relative humidity, odour, electromagnetic interference? If so, state levels of tolerance.

11.3 Space

11.3.1 Floor area

• What is the minimum floor area, in net usable square metres, to reasonably accommodate the activities, as calculated by the brief writer?

11.3.2 Relationships

What key requirements for proximity does this space have in relation to other spaces? This information confirms the relationship matrix and relationship. The brief writer, understanding planning, will discourage any clients' tendency to request many relationships.

11.3.3 Enclosure

What degree of enclosure is required?

• complete, enclosed by four walls
• partial enclosure, always open to an adjoining space
• interconnecting, capable of opening onto an adjoining space

11.3.4 Access

- What dimensions of door opening will accommodate the largest object likely to pass through?
- What degree of door security is required?

11.3.5 Layout diagram

A simple diagram, rather than a design, demonstrates that the area allowed is appropriate and that the furniture and equipment both accommodates appropriate relationships between them and allows space for change. (See example in Figure 11.1.)

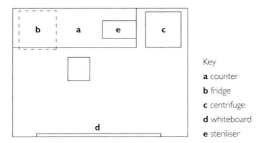

Key
a counter
b fridge
c centrifuge
d whiteboard
e steriliser

Figure 11.1 Typical space layout diagram

11.3.6 Special structural features

Are there any exceptional requirements for ceiling heights, floor loading, or other structural features?

11.4 Interior environment

This section may be filled out twice: first to define standards for the building as a whole, and secondly to define standards where there are exceptional functional requirements space by space. In these cases, the brief will state the reason and specify a performance standard, possibly following specialist consultants' advice. The reason and standard should relate to policies defined in Chapter 10. The brief will state whether standards are mandatory or just desirable. Standards for daylighting, artificial lighting, heating and cooling are currently under review as the balance between expected comfort levels, levels of provision, cost and environmental implications is reassessed.

11.4.1 Daylight

Is there a special functional requirement for:

- daylight as opposed to artificial light, or the reverse, beyond personal preference
- functional requirements for shading or other precautions against glare blackout?

The brief should define mean and minimum daylight factors or levels and light quality.[2]

11.4.2 Views

Is there a specific functional requirement for:

- internal views
- external views
- privacy from other internal spaces
- privacy from outside?

11.4.3 Artificial lighting

Are there any functional requirements for:

- special lighting or controls
- task lighting
- lighting control: movement sensing, timed, zoned, individual control (this is in order to minimise energy wastage)?

Minimum and target luminance should be defined in lux and luminance ratio.[3]

11.4.4 Environmental comfort

Are there any special functional requirements for:

- heating
- cooling
- relative humidity
- ventilation (natural or artificial)
- controls for any of the above
- opening windows, for particular categories of user?

The brief should explain functional purposes served, such as: removal of odour, or CO_2; cooling.

It should define mean, minimum and maximum design values for winter and summer, noting that the wider the design range, the less the necessity to depart from natural or low energy solutions:

- temperature ranges (°C)
- ventilation rate (air changes per minute or hour, m^3/min, or l/s)
- air movement ranges (m/s)
- relative humidity (%)

11.4.5 Acoustics

Are there any functional requirements for:

- acoustic separation from noise sources
- acoustic separation for privacy
- specific acoustics characteristics?

The brief should define sound reduction (in dB) and other characteristics.

11.4.6 Finishes

Are there any functional requirements for special finishes to:

- walls
- floor
- ceiling
- doors?

Requirements may include: non-slip, high or low reflectivity, wipe-down, wash-down, anti-bacterial, non-allergenic.

11.5 Services

The brief should note requirements for any of the following services:

11.5.1 Electrical power

- quantity of non-dedicated double outlets for small equipment

- quantity of outlets dedicated to named equipment items
- quantity of fused spur supplies

Table 11.2 Example of table of power requirements

Purpose	Outlet type	Qty	Comments
Example:			
non-dedicated, small equipment	double 13 A	6	
computer + monitor etc	double 13 A	4	dedicated circuit, UPS
sterilisation unit	fused spur	1	backup generator

For each, the brief should comment on any special types of supply: three-phase; non-standard voltage; dedicated circuit; priority for backup generation; uninterruptible power supply (UPS); special earths etc.

11.5.2 Communications and IT

- internal/external phone, voice and data
- internal and external computer networks
- linked mobile communications
- fax
- paging
- CCTV
- satellite TV
- entry systems
- bells and signals
- other communications systems

11.5.3 Other low-voltage systems

- fire
- intruder alarm
- other security
- environmental sensing
- other

The brief should note requirements for any of the following services, purpose, quality, control, delivery location, and any special features:

11.5.4 Water

- domestic hot water

- cold water – domestic cold, cold, drinking, deionised, demineralised, distilled etc.
- drains

Table 11.3 Example of table of piped services

Service	Purpose	Location	Comments
cold water	general	sink	
distilled water	lab processes	sink	
air	lab processes	work bench	lab quality

11.5.5 Gases

- air – industrial, laboratory, medical
- steam
- vacuum – wet, dry, medical
- piped or bottled gases

11.5.6 Air extract

The brief should note any special treatment of extract air:

- mechanical ventilation
- canopy
- fume cupboard

11.5.7 Non-IT distribution systems

- paper distribution systems
- small item distribution
- large items or bulk distribution

11.6 Furniture and equipment

11.6.1 Loose furniture

The brief should list each piece of loose furniture required in this space, quantity, approximate dimensions and any special features.

Table 11.4 Example of table of loose furniture

Item	Qty	Length (mm)	Width (mm)	Height (mm)	Comments
lab stool	I			650 – 850	gas lift, back, wipe-down upholstery, footrest
visitor chair	I				wipe-down surfaces

11.6.2 Equipment

The brief should list each piece of equipment that requires floor or counter space, or which has a requirement for electrical power or other services, together with quantity, approximate dimensions and any special features.

Table 11.5 Example of table of equipment

Item	Qty	Length (mm)	Width(mm)	Height (mm)	Comments
centrifuge	I	550	650	800	on floor 240 V, single phase
fridge	I	600	600	850	below counter, 240 V, single phase
sterilisation unit	I	400	600	350	counter top, 240 V, single phase

11.6.3 Fixtures

The brief should list requirements for major fixtures with their sizes, as shown in Table 11.6.

Table 11.6 Example of table of fixtures

Item	Qty	Length (mm)	Width(mm)	Height (mm)	Comments
coathook strip	I				wall hung, 3 hooks
counter	I	2000	600	900	kneehole +2 bays x 4 lockable drawers belowscrub-down top.
whiteboard	I	2000		900	

I   A checklist of space data sheets is the stock in trade of briefing consultants, and there are many variations. This checklist has been developed from one prepared some years ago by the author together with colleagues M. Galloway Scott, A. McCready, D. Nesbitt, J. Wilson and W. Wood
2   *Recommended daylight factors* (CIBSE, 1987)
3   *CIBSE UK Guide*

12 Proposal, brief document, testing

The three annotated checklists presented in this chapter, like those in other chapters, are generic and must be customised to the particular project. They are:

- proposal
- brief document
- testing

12.1 Proposal

Written succinctly and direct to the point, a proposal is necessary even if there is no external client to satisfy; the proposal defines the plan of work for the briefing exercise. Here is a typical proposal outline:

- Summary – a short paragraph stating the project name, cost, start and completion dates and the name of the briefing consultant's firm.
- Introduction – used to state what the project is, and at whose invitation it has been written.
- Background – a short paragraph to show understanding of the clients' problem, and their reasons for initiating the project. The situation as they see it is briefly summarised.
- Goal and objectives – states the single goal of the project and the more detailed objectives that come under it. This paragraph includes the project limits or parameters.
- Approach – describes briefly how the consultant will tackle the project. It will include any special surveys or studies by external consultants, as well as the proposed structure of client or user working groups or committees.
- Tasks – sets out a list of tasks to complete the project. These will be used as the basis for resourcing, budget and programme. Tasks to be carried out by the client and by specialists are described, whether as part of the project team or not.
- Deliverables – lists the products of the project, such as an illustrated report, a presentation to the board, copies of the presentation, a workshop for the local community, etc., stating the purpose of each.
- Programme – shows a simple barchart with tasks listed against date and duration. Project milestones such as major meetings and report delivery dates are highlighted. The programme will be used to calculate resourcing for the project team.
- Cost – shows the total project cost. It is customary to give a breakdown of hours and hourly rates for team members. A contingency sum should be

allowed, to cover the unexpected. Its size will depend on an appraisal of project risks and of the market for briefing services. The consultant must be clear about the degree of project risk that he or she is offering to accept. A percentage is allowed for project expenses, and payment terms are stated.

- Project team – introduces the project team, with a paragraph on each member, describing qualifications and relevant experience and referring, if appropriate, to fuller CVs in an appendix. The role of each member of the team in the project is stated.
- Appendix – carries more detailed information on any of the above sections. It may contain one-page CVs for team members, or brochures for the consultant's firm or for any external consultants on the team.

12.2 Brief document contents

A typical list of contents for a brief is shown below. For a small project some sections would be covered by a single line, and others by a short paragraph. In a large project that short paragraph may be appropriate, or it may become several pages.

- Cover
- Contents list
- Executive summary, which tells the whole story on no more than a single side, and is all that top management are likely to read
- Introduction, including background, project history, work completed, acknowledgement of participants, as appropriate
- This report, explaining what is in the brief and how to access it as a reference
- Role statement, as described in Chapter 1
- Activity descriptions, as described above. This may contain a flow diagram of activities and details of people numbers, present and projected
- Requirements, as described above, with facility guidelines and facility requirements. This may include a matrix and diagram of relationships between spaces. A list of spaces and their floor areas is essential
- Cost – giving estimates for various options within the brief and for the preferred option
- Programme – a single construction programme or options for phasing construction
- Appendices, including such material as detailed spreadsheets, interview notes, photocopies of clients' own records, as appropriate
- Sign-off sheet. Sometimes a formal acknowledgement that the brief meets the requirements of the steering committee and working groups is useful. It documents the completion of the consultant's work and authorises the final brief document as the basis for design. It is signed by top management when the brief has been tested and amended

12.3 Checklist for testing

This checklist applies in principle to the testing step that occurs at each repetition of the briefing process, though there are questions that will be more relevant in some cases than in others.

Table 12.1 Checklist for testing a building brief

12.3.1 Accuracy and consistency	• Does the brief accurately document the briefing process, and is it internally consistent?
12.3.2 Fit	• Can the required space be provided within the site or existing building?
12.3.3 Budget	• Is the projected cost within budget?
12.3.4 Business case	• Is the project commercially sound and good value?
12.3.5 Programme	• Can the project be built to the required programme?
12.3.6 Technical feasibility	• Is the project technically feasible and buildable?
12.3.7 Impacts	• Are the impacts of the project acceptable?
12.3.8 Procurement route	• How will the project be realised, and what are the implications?
12.3.9 Statutory compliance	• Does the proposed project comply with statutory regulations and policies?
12.3.10 Resources	• Are appropriately skilled people available to the project?

12.3.1 Accuracy and consistency

- Does the brief accurately document the discussion and decisions made during the briefing process?
- Is the argument for a building meeting these requirements clear and unassailable from an operational point of view?
- Is the argument internally consistent, with any conflicting objectives resolved?
- Are the corporate aims and objectives of the role statement reflected in activities and requirements to support them?
- Are there rogue requirements without logical basis? This is an opportunity to distinguish between what people have said they want and what is actually needed in relation to policy and objectives. It is the moment to finally weed out any 'Christmas wishlists'.
- Are there idiosyncratic requirements that are not consistent with best practice for the industry sector? If so, is this understood and approved by the clients?
- Are there objectives that are not provided for in the brief requirements?

12.3.2 Fit

- Will the floor area requirement fit on the chosen site or within the existing building or a new one?
- Will it not only fit, but is it feasible when tested against the constraints, opportunities, characteristics and quirks of the site or existing building?
- Is a building evaluation or site assessment required?
- Is a more detailed site survey or specialist investigation required?

12.3.3 Budget

In most cases a quantity surveyor will be able to provide a cost estimate based on a draft brief to within around 5% either way, albeit with a number of provisos.

- Is it feasible to build within a budget that is prudently available and already earmarked in the organisational business plan?
- Are the funds available to complete the project?

12.3.4 Business case

- Is the construction project commercially sound? Does it add sufficient value in relation to the investment and borrowing cost?
- Does this option represent the best currently available value for the organisation in terms of its needs and objectives, providing more and better space for present and future operations?
- Is the project as a whole compatible with best practice in the industry sector?
- Will the project enhance the marketplace competitiveness of the client organisation?
- Is the commercial risk of the project understood and acceptable?
- Are the risks to business continuity understood and acceptable?
- If the organisation hits financial problems, will the space be lettable or saleable on completion, given the location and possible property market conditions?

12.3.5 Programme

- Can the project be built in the required time?
- Is the programme feasible considering any needs for:
- completing construction in a series of separate phases over time
- building over time in zoned areas of the site, and
- decanting users and functions to temporary accommodation during construction?

12.3.6 Technical feasibility

- Is it technically feasible to put up such a building? Is it buildable?
- Is the construction risk inherent in the project understood and manageable?
- Are the construction health and safety risks understood and manageable?

12.3.7 Impacts

- What will be the impact of this building on its immediate neighbourhood, on the locality, and in terms of global environmental concerns?
- Are the objectives for sustainable development written into the brief consistent with the environmental objectives and commitments of the organisation, and are they consistent with best practice within its industry sector?

12.3.8 Procurement route

The probable procurement route will have influenced the way briefing is carried out right from the start. By the testing stage, a decision on procurement should have been taken, and it is likely that a prime contractor, a project manager or other professional advisor will be involved in the process. The consultant checks at this stage that the needs of the professional advisor and prime contractor are met by the brief.

12.3.9 Statutory compliance

- Does the proposed project fit within local planning guidelines, and what is likely to be required to ensure that planning permission is achieved?
- Are there any features in the requirements that are likely to be problematic in maintaining compliance with building regulations and other statutory controls?

12.3.10 Resources

- Does the design team have the appropriate experience and expertise to carry out the work? Has this been proven? Have references been taken up?
- In particular, does the design team contain experts in environmental analysis and design, for projects where this is a crucial issue?
- Does the clients' project team have adequate and experienced resources to manage the project? What steps are being taken to remedy any shortfall?

12.3.11 Commitment

Finally, if the design team produces a building that meets the requirements documented in this brief, does the client group really like it and want it? Are they committed to go ahead with the project as described in the brief? Will it meet the needs of this client group and the needs of those who will succeed them?

13 Case histories

The checklists given in the last three chapters have been comprehensive, listing most of the issues that should be considered in larger projects. In order to describe how the briefing process can be adapted to projects of all sizes, this chapter describes briefing exercises for three typical smaller projects. In each, the checklists have been edited to focus on relevant issues together with others that are project-specific. As the projects get larger, briefing becomes more formal. The projects are fictitious but are based on experience. They are:

- a 15 m^2 bathroom – a typical domestic renovation
- a 150 m^2 clothing shop – a small commercial renovation
- a 1500 m^2 office – a building brief rather than a fitting-out brief, for a new-build project, where the client is the prospective pre-let tenant

13.1 A 15 m^2 bathroom

This briefing project, the smallest of the three, is described quite informally. Background information about the project is mixed with briefing information, and much of the earlier parts of the process were not formally documented. However informal, the whole briefing process is there in miniature, and section titles are noted in brackets at the end of the paragraphs to which they refer.

From the client's initial call, the architect had already worked out that a spare bedroom in the client's Victorian house could probably be converted into a second bathroom. On a first visit it became clear that her plan was to use the existing bathroom for house guests and the new one for herself. (*Statement of need and option appraisal*)

The house had been valued, and the architect had an estimated value for the house with the additional bathroom. He had considered the client's moving to a house with two bathrooms, but calculated that the additional bathroom would add value to her existing house, which she was very content with in other ways, despite the loss of a bedroom. He was clear that the decision was based on her preference rather than on financial calculations. Finance had been arranged for an appropriate sum. He envisaged the work being carried out by a small contractor using a traditional contract. He thought that it should be possible to start work in April and complete by July. (*Strategic brief*)

As a buyer for a large retail chain, the client travelled frequently on business. She lived alone in a degree of comfort, and wished to entertain out-of-town friends and oversees business associates in her home for short visits, while maintaining a private space for herself. (*Brief, role statement*)

Her early morning regime was really important to her; she had developed it over some time to prepare herself for the day. It consisted of a session on an exercise bike, and showering, before dressing, meditating, and going down for breakfast. She returned to see to teeth, hair and make-up before leaving for work. When she returned from work she wanted the possibility of a bath with subdued lighting and aromatherapy oils. She sometimes returned briefly in the early evening to shower and change before going out to an evening engagement. On occasions the bathroom would need to accommodate two people. Together the client and architect developed a programme of typical morning bathroom use:

- 5.30 am   rise
- 5.35–6.55   exercise bike, preferably in bathroom
- 5.55–6.15   shower and dress
- 6.15–6.45   meditate, in bedroom
- 6.45–7.00   breakfast, in kitchen
- 7.00–7.15   teeth, hair and make-up, in bathroom
- 7.20   leave for work

Similar programmes were developed for early evening and bedtime. It became clear from this that the timing and efficiency of the morning routine were crucial. (*Brief, activity description*)

The client said that she needed a spacious room that was simple but elegant, from which she could emerge refreshed in the morning, prepared to face a very busy day, and be able to relax in the evening. She saw lighting as important, especially making use of the east-facing window. A second lighting scheme would give a subdued effect in the evening. She wondered whether it would be feasible to recycle bath water to use in the toilet. She was concerned that the room should be warm enough to walk into directly from the bedroom early in the morning. All the surfaces should be easy to reach and wipe down. (*Brief, facility guidelines*)

Using the detailed design brief checklist, the following notes were made of detailed requirements:

- The available floor area was measured at 15 m².
- Access was to be only directly from the bedroom.
- The room should remain separate from the bedroom; enlargement of the window opening should be considered. (*Brief, requirements, space*)
- Views out were not necessary, but early morning light was important to the client.
- A morning and an evening lighting scheme were required as well as a dim light

for night-time visits. Light fittings should be concealed. Heating to the room should be independently controllable at a range between 18°C and 22°C.
- Ventilation should be automatic but with a manual override to allow high humidity during aromatherapy sessions.
- Finishes should be easy to wipe down, with stone or ceramic tile to floors and walls, and large mirrored wall areas. (*Brief, requirements, interior environment*)
- A shaver outlet was required, and speakers linked to the music system already installed in the bedroom.
- The shower was to have a power shower feature.
- The bath was to have a bubble action feature. (*Brief, requirements, services*)
- Fixtures and fittings:
  - bath, 2000 x 800 mm rectangular preferred
  - screened shower area, 900 x 1200 mm minimum
  - WC, reduced flush, possible using recycled grey water or rainwater
  - bidet
  - two wash-basins
  - separate storage for towels, cleaning materials and toiletries
  - make-up area next to the wash-basin with counter top, mirror and storage
  - if possible, a place should be made for the exercise bike.
    (*Brief, requirements, fixtures and fittings*)

Before leaving, the architect mentioned that planning permission would be needed for the enlarged window, as the house was in a conservation area. He inspected the electrical distribution board and reported that there was adequate electrical capacity for the demands of the new bathroom. A larger hot water cylinder would be required. Space for storage of grey and rainwater would be investigated. He agreed to make a budget check on the basis of the brief, and to prepare some preliminary design ideas, to test that, in principle, there was sufficient space for the desired functions. (*Testing*)

Client and architect met a week later, with these checks complete. The architect gave an estimate of costs, and reported that technically the project was feasible and that planning permission was probably achievable. He produced a flow diagram, based on the client's own description of her morning routine. This showed a preferred relationship of functional areas to each other and to the entrance to the bathroom. There was a conflict between the requirement for the WC to be the first used and the need to separate it from the bedroom. It was felt this could be resolved in the design. Based on this diagram, he showed a simple sketch that demonstrated that the requirements would fit, provided that one or more of the functions were dropped. There was a conflict between the number of fittings and the design guideline, 'spacious ... simple and elegant'. It was agreed to proceed with a single wash-basin and to leave the exercise bike in the bedroom. The client authorised the architect to continue to the design stage on the basis of the amended brief. (*Approval*)

13.2 A 150 m² clothing shop

This project is described more formally, but again background information about the project for the benefit of the reader is interspersed with briefing information. Here section headings define the stages in briefing. The architect does not come on the scene until the statement of need and option appraisal have been completed. In fact the client had not been aware that these stages existed until the architect asked the questions that produced the information described below.

13.2.1 Statement of need

The client was a fashion designer who designed, manufactured and sold women's clothes in a provincial city. His aim was to open a second operation in London. The new shop would be arranged with the same elements as the existing one, containing a showroom, workshop and office, plus support areas.

13.2.2 Option appraisal

The client and his accountant had prepared a business plan. The client took it to his bank, where the manager was impressed by the turnover of the first shop and its low level of indebtedness. The manager agreed a loan to cover setting up the new shop, but success depended on a rapid increase in turnover once it was open. The client visited several London estate agents and saw a number of premises in different areas before finding an unusual vacant shop in an up-and-coming inner London neighbourhood. He felt the location was promising, and could only improve. The interior clearly needed a lot of work, but it had potential. In addition to a large double-height showroom area it had a well-lit area at the rear, which would be ideal for workshop and office. He calculated that, if the interiors were kept very simple, the fit-out would be affordable.

13.2.3 Context

At this point the architect was engaged, and his immediate concern was not with the building, but with the management of the operation. At the initial discussion, he realised that the whole business rested on the shoulders of the owner, who personally carried out the functions of design, manufacture and sales with the help of three assistants. The very individual style of his work extended to the interior design of the first shop, and the style in which customers were served. It depended on the owner's taking the lead role in all activities. While this worked in a single location, the architect questioned how it could work in two separate locations. The client replied that, in time, he would find the right people to fill the positions in the way he wanted, and would split his own time between the two locations.

13.2.4 Role

'The purpose of the London shop is to bring the collections and the philosophy behind them to a wider public.' There was then a series of objectives: target customer groups, projections for turnover and units sold per month, an annual programme for designing new collections, and targets for manufacturing the garments.

13.2.5 Activities

Activities were easily grouped into four main functions: selling, manufacture, design and administration. In addition there were support functions: storage, a utility area for wet manufacturing processes, a small kitchen, shower and toilet. A minimum of two and maximum of six staff would work there at any one time, moving between the functions.

The aim of the showroom was to display clothes simply, so that they spoke for themselves. Almost all the stock would be on display. In the showroom, customers could examine and try on the collection in a variety of sizes and colours. The showroom would be staffed by one or two people, who also worked in other areas. It was important for staff to be able to move quickly from one area to another, and especially to attend customers entering the showroom. A survey of customer numbers at the first shop was carried out by an assistant under the architect's direction. It showed that the showroom was empty for 20% of opening hours, had one customer for 40%, up to three customers for 35%, and three to six customers at peak times (5% of opening hours). 50% of customers were accompanied by family or friends. See Figure 13.1.

Figure 13.1 Average numbers of customers in the showroom

The workshop would accommodate up to four people engaged in cutting, machine sewing, hand finishing, pressing, and other manufacturing tasks. Storage was required for threads, trimmings and small components, for cloth in immediate use, for some finished garments, and for those awaiting alteration.

The office would accommodate two people: the owner and a part-time bookkeeper. It would not be staffed all the time. It would support functions such as bookkeeping and payroll, ordering, personnel interviews, computer design, design of promotional material, and website design.

Support functions: A small tea kitchen would serve staff and sometimes customers. Some of the manufacturing processes included wet treatments of fabric and laundering of cloth and garments. Bolts of cloth and packaging materials would be stored away from the manufacturing function.

There were peaks each year when the new seasonal collections were launched, a Christmas rush and sales in January and July. At these times staff would be deployed in the showroom rather than in the workshop, and alterations would be subcontracted to home-workers.

13.2.6 Facility guidelines

The client had a clear view of the ambiance he wanted to create: welcoming and non-threatening, avoiding fashion snobbery and intimidating chic. He wanted his customers to know that he understood them, their beauty and potential, their insecurities and imperfect bodies. He knew his designs were striking enough to attract young women but would cope equally with the realistic shape of the mature woman.

The workshop and office should be out of sight of the customer in the showroom, but the showroom and entrance should be easily overseen.

The shopfront should be simple, elegant, modern, but not hard edged. It should give an inviting view into the showroom, past a simple window display.

13.2.7 Space

The architect made a measured survey of the premises that the client had chosen. The ground floor showroom measured 100 m^2, and the rear workshop, support areas and offices 50 m^2.

- The workshop should be completely enclosed to contain the noise from sewing machines, and to contain fluff produced during manufacture.
- Easy access was required to the showroom from workshop and office.
- Support areas should be concealed at the rear of the showroom.
- Three changing rooms should be generously sized, unobtrusive and separated by a curtained entrance.

Space requirements:

Total available space 150 m^2
Area required in m^2:

showroom	75
changing rooms	9
wheelchair toilet	4
tea kitchen	4
utility area	5
storage	8
office	10
workshop	35

Total area required 150 m^2

Note that circulation is in this case included within the listed areas.

13.2.8 Interior environment

- Daylight – Important in workshop, but otherwise not important
- View – Required to the showroom from workshop and office, from office to workshop, and into showroom from street
- Artificial lighting
  - showroom: warm ambient lighting and display lighting in showroom
  - workshop: ambient and tungsten task lighting
  - office: cat 5 lighting
- display lighting to window display
- Environmental comfort – Temperature control important, 18° to 24°C to showroom. Underfloor heating or air-conditioning probably required in the showroom. Floors and walls of showroom to be kept clear of mechanical equipment. Mechanical ventilation required, and a problem of air pollution at the street frontage.
- Acoustics – Machine noise to be contained in workshop. Acoustics in showroom to be soft, despite hard surface required of floors and walls.
- Finishes – Simple, low-cost finishes

- walls: plaster, matt white paint
- floor: hard surface, stone, tile or wood

It might be argued that finishes should be left to the design architect, but in this case the client had a clear vision that he wanted to realise.

13.2.9 Services

The schedule of electrical requirements is listed in Table 13.1.

- Communications
  - two telephone lines to office, with extensions to showroom and workshop; consider cordless system
  - audible signal at entrance door
  - intruder alarm
  - security CCTV
- Water – domestic hot and cold water, to utility, kitchen, shower and toilet
- Heating/cooling
  - hot water heating to mezzanine and support areas
  - underfloor heating to show room
  - comfort cooling to all areas
  - exhausts from toilet, shower and utility area

Table 13.1 From schedule of electrical requirements

Space	Purpose	Qty	Comments
showroom	general	8	all 13 A double outlets
kitchen	fridge, kettle, microwave	4	
utility	portable equipment	2	
workshop	4 sewing machines, 2 irons, 1 steam iron, 6 task lights	10	
office	2 computers, 2 printers, 6 peripherals, copier, fax	8	
mechanical	electrical service to mechanical plant		hot water, under floor or a/c, heating to mezzanine, ventilation and exhausts from kitchen, utility, shower and toilet

13.2.10 Furniture and equipment

The schedule of furniture and equipment is demonstrated in Table 13.2.

Table 13.2 Schedule of furniture and equipment

Item	Qty	L (mm)	W (mm)	H (mm)	Comments
office					
desk	2	1800	1400	720	L shaped, 800 mm deep, wipe-down top
desk chairs	2				orthopaedic, adjustable
printer stand etc	2	600	600	720	with stationery storage below

13.3 A 1500 m² office

A specialist insurance company was located in a small town, where it was expanding steadily. With 85 staff, it had outgrown a rabbit warren of space in adjoining converted town houses and needed new space. Because of its reliance on networked computers it had decided to look for 1500 m² of modern office space to lease. (*Statement of need*)

It did not take the company long to conclude that there was no available space to lease in the town, but a local estate agent put them in touch with a developer who had a vacant site in the run-down industrial district.

13.3.1 Option appraisal

They considered their options:

Option A: Do nothing
They would run out of space within 18 months. The quality of the existing space was poor, and a disincentive to staff. The electrical and cabling infrastructure were running close to capacity; major renovations would be required if they were to be substantially extended. The building overheated on hot summer days, when reduced productivity was demonstrable.

Option B: Relocate to a nearby city
Office space was available in a city 40 miles away. They calculated that:
- Rents would be considerably higher than they expected to pay in the town.
- Up to two thirds of staff would probably choose not to commute by car or relocate, and this would include some senior people on whom the business depended.
- Time lost and the expense of travel for the remaining third would be significant.
- Available office space was of a reasonable quality.
- Parking was limited in the city centre.
- Connection to the motorway was better from the town than from the city.

Option C: Lease custom-built space from the developer in the town
- There would be a delay of two years for design and construction.
- The design would meet the company's needs.
- There would not be any relocation problems of staff loss or transport costs.
- Rents would be affordable.
- The services infrastructure and environmental quality would be vastly improved.

The options were costed, and Option C was chosen.

13.3.2 Strategic brief

The management group realised that they did not have the necessary skills to negotiate terms and requirements with the developer. They called on a senior architect to take the role of client adviser to guide them through the process, and then undertook the following tasks:

- review the business plan, making allowances for costs associated with the new space and of interim arrangements
- set out to find additional temporary space to meet requirements up to occupancy of the new building
- develop an IT and services strategy to meet interim needs
- inform staff of their intentions, in order to quell rumours (staff were promised a bright future in return for a degree of continuing discomfort in the short term)
- take the opportunity of reviewing working practices and bringing them up to date with latest thinking:
  - to increase staff productivity and enjoyment of work
  - to make the best use of the existing space in the interim period
  - to prepare for a new culture and better ways of working following the move

Following this exercise, the client adviser suggested that specialist consultants should be engaged to help them with defining requirements for the new building – in other words, to produce a brief.

The briefing consultant met with the director responsible (the project sponsor), and was shown around the existing office space. The consultant's subsequent proposal was accepted by the clients, and the briefing exercise commenced.

13.3.3 Role

The role statement consisted of three sentences. A longer paragraph defined the roles of each department. The activity analysis was more substantial. The present organisation and staffing were recorded, and projections were made for 5 and 10 years ahead. In this, three scenarios were developed: in one it was assumed that growth would continue at the same rate as that of the last 5 years, in a second that it would level off at roughly the present rate, and in a third that there would be a decline in staff numbers after year 2. This would be due to greater automation, to a larger proportion of Internet business, or to an economic downturn. The cost implications of each scenario were calculated. It was important that a feasible business case could be made in the worst-case scenario. (*Sensitivity analysis*)

The role of each of the four departments was defined during interviews with department heads. Meanwhile, at the next meeting with the client working group, progress was made in defining objectives for transforming the culture of the company to be more responsive to clients and the market, more supportive of staff, more relaxed and flexible, and to make more demands of staff initiative and teamwork.

Possible scenarios for growth and change were again discussed and confirmed.

It was decided that the new building would conform to standards of good to excellent on the BREEAM schedule of sustainability benchmarks. A director would be appointed to develop policies and monitor performance on sustainability in all areas of the business operations both before and after the move to the new building.

The consultant was asked to review the implications of the site, looking in particular at transport, parking, and the possibility of enhancing the surrounding environment. There was very little open green space nearby.

There was some discussion of image and appearance, and the client group realised that, beyond personal preferences, no one had thought about their office space in those terms. The director with a responsibility for publicity and marketing would be asked to set up a meeting between the briefing consultant and the company's marketing consultants to develop policies for image and appearance that reflected the company's brand image in the eyes of both customers and staff. This last exercise developed into a re-branding exercise.

13.3.4 Activities

The consultant was provided with an organisation chart that identified full-time staff, contractors and part-timers. Interviews with directors had produced descriptions of activities for each department, including frequencies and sizes of meetings. Seasonal peaks for various types of work and methods of coping with them were also discussed. Quantities, types and frequencies of visitors were identified. Finally the meeting discussed current management issues, such as moving to newly developed software, developing and integrating the company website into operations, and finding solutions to operational problems resulting from the lack of capacity in the existing building.

The company was committed to growth, and the consultant was informed in confidence that it would actively pursue expansion by acquisition.

Alongside interviews with directors and key people such as the IT manager, meetings were held with small groups of staff in each department to understand what worked well at present and what did not, and what staff would like to see in the new building. This information was complemented by an activity survey over several days, which established the information shown in Figure 13.2.

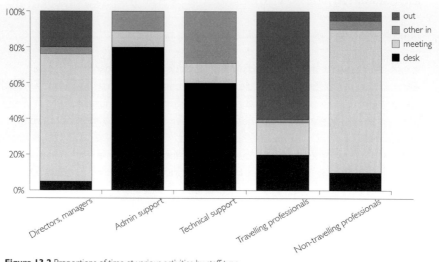

Figure 13.2 Proportions of time at various activities by staff type

13.3.5 Interim accommodation

As briefing progressed, a plan was developed to accommodate staff growth in the period to occupancy of the new building. The consultant calculated that, by fine-tuning the existing space, it could just accommodate projected growth in the interim. This involved bringing forward preliminary recommendations for changes to operations and image prior to the move. The plan included:

- minor alterations
- creating more meeting rooms
- new, smaller furniture that would be reused in the new building
- workstations in open office space for all
- 'hot desks' for a proportion of travelling professionals
- a small call centre in the customer services department
- reducing storage through central filing, archiving and electronic document management
- improved staff amenities including soft seating areas with coffee adjacent

It was agreed to proceed on this basis as the improvement would be significant, even though some overcrowding was projected in the last 9 months before occupancy.

Staff representatives felt that reduced standards would be acceptable for a limited period. Note that this exercise was not part of the briefing process, but a necessary additional consultancy service, which was identified and billed as such.

13.3.6 Design guidelines

Design guidelines for the new building first considered transport. The clients' objective was to encourage use of public transport and bicycles for the journey to work. Cycle racks and showers would be provided. Car parking would be required for travelling staff. A car drop-off area and loading area for delivery vans were required.

Security was an issue, and access control was required as well as CCTV monitoring. A higher level of internal security was specified for the computer and telecoms rooms. High gates would protect the car park area at night. A separate study recommended specifications for physical resilience of building and services.

The major part of the space would be office space, with specific structural requirements:

- 80% of net internal area (NIA) to be within 6 m of windows
- frequency of columns to be no less than 50 m^2 of NIA per column
- floor-to-ceiling height to be no less than 2.8 m on upper floors, 3.3 m on ground floor
- 300 mm minimum raised floor, with all panels accessible
- ground and first floors to have independent access to permit subletting if necessary in units of 100 m^2
- loading bay accessible by refuse vehicles, with adjacent waste-holding area, ground floor storage and separate goods lift
- ground floor reception area with wheelchair access from street and throughout

In terms of image and quality, the client required a standard of provision higher than was customary in a small town. The standard of finishes and local services was to be defined in a brief for detailed fitting out. The branding consultants had proposed the following key words along with a collage of pictorial images: friendly, efficient, accessible, responsive, reliable, supportive, well equipped, aware, problem-solving, in touch, cutting edge, best methods.

The company was expecting to grow, but required to sublet the ground and first floors initially on short leases to provide for future expansion. The overall area of the building would provide for foreseeable future needs.

The building was to be low in energy use, with CO_2 emissions less than 20 kg/m^2 per year.

The reuse of rainwater in toilets should be considered.

Building materials with long life and low embodied energy should be given preference. Weatherproofing of the building envelope should be by simple form and proven, durable materials rather than by complex detailing.

Natural cooling with high thermal mass was preferred, with careful control of heat gain. Fenestration should be designed so that 70% usable office area would be naturally lit through 60% of the working year. Windows were to be glare-free at all times.

The services strategy should incorporate the following:
- electrical and telephone connections to be duplicated and come from separate sources, to increase resilience
- electrical underfloor distribution to be by a continuous busbar system
- independent standby generation to be provided for 15% of the small-power load
- wet piped services to be routed away from the office floors or kept to the periphery with separation from the underfloor void

Budget and programme were subject to negotiation with the developer.

13.3.7 Requirements

Table 13.3 shows the space list that was produced to accommodate 160 staff.

There were no critical relationships between departments, except that computer and telecoms rooms were to be in the interior of the building for security and resilience.

Note that most of the checklist headings from Chapter 10 were covered. Office-specific issues were also considered. These were:

- culture
- workstation type
- storage
- machines, IT and communications
- meeting rooms and spaces
- staff amenity spaces

Culture was a company-wide issue. Other issues were considered at three levels:

- company or building support
- shared local support to workgroup or department
- individual requirements

Table 13.3 Demand for space

		total	Dept. A	Dept B	Dept. C	Dept. D
Workstations	unit area					
Staff	9	160	18	55	63	24
workstation A qty	6.5	18	8	4	6	0
workstation B qty	3	84	10	47	21	6
hot desk qty	0	17	0	2	15	0
no fixed desk qty		45	0	0	36	9
Areas – workstations		753	137	341.5	235.5	39
Local support	unit area					
	10					
meeting room 8	6.5	60	20	10	20	10
interview 2/quiet work	9	39	6.5	13	19.5	0
open meeting area 4	1.5	36	0	9	18	9
copiers, printers, fax		28	3	12	9	3
filing, stationery	1	23	8	7	8	4
coats		10	3	5	6	3
coffee /soft seating		69	12	15	30	12
Areas – local seating		265	50.5	68	106.5	40
Common support						
meeting room 30	40	80				
computer room		15				
telecoms room		10				
central photocopying		12				
reception/waiting		15				
central filling		12				
mail room		20				
maintenance room		12				
central stores		12				
waste holding area		15				
Area – common support		178				
Total area	factor					
Net usable rrea	2%	1196	188	410	342	79
Fit factor	20%	24	4	8	7	9
Primary circulation		239	38	82	68	16
Net internal area		*1459*	229	500	417	104

13.3.8 Approval

The draft brief was approved by the client subject to some minor modifications, and formed the basis for negotiations with the developer and his architect. The briefing consultant was retained to evaluate design proposals against the brief.